DIRECTORY OF
STAGE COACH SERVICES
1836

directory of
STAGE
COACH
SERVICES
1836

compiled by ALAN BATES

DAVID & CHARLES · NEWTON ABBOT

7153 4379 3

Printed in Great Britain by
Redwood Press Limited Trowbridge Wiltshire
for David & Charles (Holdings) Limited
South Devon House Railway Station
Newton Abbot Devon.

CONTENTS

INTRODUCTION

I have chosen 1836 as the year on which to base this directory of coaching, for in this year the business reached its peak, and many proprietors were engaged in a spirit of intense competition and rivalry. Although 'furious insane racing' was going on along the London to Birmingham road — as on other trunk roads — the clouds of doom were well in sight. Railway construction was in progress, and between Manchester and Liverpool, and Hexham and Blaydon, passenger trains were already working.

Although I have tried hard to ensure that the details in this book are accurate, the task of gleaning information from a multitude of directories, coaching bills and newspaper advertisements of a bygone age has produced several differences of factual information. It seems that competition caused services to be revised almost daily.

I hope this book will be as interesting to read as it has been to prepare, and trust that some details of a great art and profession may be preserved before they are buried in the passing of time.

ALAN BATES

EXPLANATORY NOTES TO TABLES

Table 1   Details of services between London and provincial places are included in this table, together with all known information regarding routes, departure times, etc. The establishments shown are the actual terminals, but it should be noted that nearly all coaches served a number of picking-up points before leaving the capital, and conversely set down at the same places upon return. Where information, such as departure time, is not known or is doubtful the space has purposely been left blank.

Table 1a   Included in this table are the coaches which are known to have operated, but for which insufficient information is available to show them in Table 1.

Table 1b   The branch coaches were used mainly to provide guaranteed connections with West End booking offices and coaches terminating in the City.

Table 1c   In only a few cases were the coaches actually owned by the proprietors. Most were owned and maintained by coachbuilders, who hired them out to the proprietors on a mileage basis.

Table 1d   This table is self-explanatory.

Table 1e   The offices shown in this table are those known to have been used as picking-up points for long-distance and/or local coaches, as mentioned in the notes for Table 1 above.

Table 2   Although the horses and coachmen for Royal Mail coaches were supplied by the contractors, the coaches and guards were provided by the Postmaster-General. Time was of prime importance and as well as carrying a blunderbuss the guards were supplied with a chronometer, which was sealed before departure. All mail coaches ran half-an-hour earlier on Sundays.

Table 2a   The schedules on these mail services were usually based on the arrival or departure of London mails.

Table 3   Grouped together in this table are all the cross-country and local services outside London. Unfortunately no information is available regarding services operating wholly within Wales and Scotland.

Table 4   Known as the 'short stages' these coaches, of various shape and size — some relegated from more arduous work — provided an intensive network of services in London and the surrounding area.

In Tables 1, 1a, 3 and 4 the use of such information as

'2216 (4 – 11)'

refers a) to the licence number, allocated by the Commissioners for the Affairs of Stamps and displayed on a plate on the coach, and b) to the seating capacity of the coach. The example above shows that the coach with plate number 2216 was licensed to carry four passengers inside and eleven outside, that is, on top. Royal Mail coaches were exempt from duty and did not carry plates.

TABLE 1
LONG-DISTANCE STAGE COACHES
FROM & TO LONDON

2145 (4-11) J. Winch & Co.

'THE SOVEREIGN'

LONDON - KEW - RICHMOND - TWICKENHAM - TEDDINGTON - HAMPTON COURT - MOLESEY - WALTON - WEYBRIDGE - ADDLESTONE (23 miles).

LONDON Blossoms Inn, Lawrence Lane	dep. 3 30 p.m.
ADDLESTONE	dep. 8 00 a.m.

Journey time : 4 hours

1901 (4-11) A. Collyer & Co.

'COLLYER'S ALTON COACH'

LONDON - KINGSTON - ESHER - GUILDFORD - FARNHAM - ALTON (49 miles).

LONDON Belle Sauvage, Ludgate Hill	dep. 11 00 a.m.	Tu, Th, Sat.
ALTON	dep.	Mon, Wed., Fri.

Journey time : 6½ hours

ADDITIONAL JOURNEYS : 2179 (4-8) 1 ret. jny. on Mon. and Sat.

3437 (4-8) W. Smith & Co.

LONDON - EDGWARE - ELSTREE - ST. ALBANS - HARPENDEN - LUTON - SILSOE - AMPTHILL (45 miles).

LONDON Three Cups, Aldersgate Street	dep. 2 00 p.m. Tu, Th, Sat.
AMPTHILL	dep. 9 00 a.m. Mon, Wed., Fri.

Journey time : 6 hours

3111, 3112 (6-12) J. Hearn & Co.

'THE DESPATCH'

LONDON - EDGWARE - STANMORE - WATFORD - HEMEL HEMPSTEAD - BERKHAMSTED - TRING - AYLESBURY (40½ miles).

LONDON Kings Arms, Snow Hill	dep. 2 00 p.m.
AYLESBURY	dep. 7 00 a.m

Journey time : 7 hours

2913 (4-11) J. Hearn & Co.

'THE UNION'

LONDON - EALING - UXBRIDGE - AMERSHAM - WENDOVER - AYLESBURY - WINSLOW - BUCKINGHAM - BRACKLEY - BANBURY (77 miles).

LONDON Kings Arms, Snow Hill	dep. 8 45 a.m. Tu., Th, Sat.
BANBURY	dep. Mon, Wed., Fri.

Journey time : 9 hours

4371, 4372, 4373 (4-8) W. Chaplin & Co.
                    'THE EXPRESS'
LONDON - WALTHAM CROSS - HODDESDON - HERTFORD - STEVENAGE -
BALDOCK - BIGGLESWADE - EATON SOCON - NORMAN CROSS -
PETERBOROUGH - MARKET DEEPING - BOURNE - SLEAFORD - LINCOLN -
BRIGG - BARTON - UPON - HUMBER (167 miles).
        LONDON Spread Eagle, Gracechurch Street dep. 4 30p.m.
        BARTON - UPON - HUMBER Waterside   dep. 5 30p.m.
          Journey time : $21\frac{1}{2}$ hours

2008, 2009 (4-11) J. Monk
                    'MONK'S BASINGSTOKE COACH'
LONDON - HOUNSLOW - STAINES - EGHAM - BAGSHOT - CAMBERLEY -
HARTLEY WINTNEY - ODIHAM - BASINGSTOKE (50 miles).
        LONDON Gerrard's Hall, Basing Lane dep. 8 45a.m.
        BASINGSTOKE   dep.
          Journey time : 6 hours

2091, 2092 (4-11) W. Halcomb & Co.
                    'THE YORK HOUSE'
LONDON - HOUNSLOW - SLOUGH - MAIDENHEAD - READING - NEWBURY -
HUNGERFORD - MARLBOROUGH - CALNE - CHIPPENHAM - BATH
(108 miles)
        LONDON Belle Sauvage, Ludgate Hill dep. 6 15a.m.
        BATH   dep. 6 30a.m.
          Journey time : 11 hours

2025, 2026 (4-11) R. Gray & Co.
                    'THE WHITE HART'
LONDON - HOUNSLOW - SLOUGH - MAIDENHEAD - READING - NEWBURY -
HUNGERFORD - MARLBOROUGH - DEVIZES - MELKSHAM - BATH
(109 miles)
        LONDON Bolt-in-Tun, Fleet Street dep. 7 00a.m.
        BATH, White Hart   dep. 7 00a.m.
          Journey time : 11 hours

3510 (4-11) B.W. Horne & Co.
                    'THE TIMES'
LONDON - BARNET - HATFIELD - HITCHIN - SHEFFORD - BEDFORD (52 miles)
        LONDON George & Blue Boar, Holborn dep. 2 00p.m.
        BEDFORD   dep. 8 30a.m.
          Journey time : 5 hours

4900 (4-11) J. Murrells

'THE TELEGRAPH'

LONDON - ILFORD - ROMFORD - BRENTWOOD - BILLERICAY (24 miles).

LONDON Bull, Aldgate   dep. 3 45 p.m.

BILLERICAY   dep. 7 45 a.m.

Journey time : 3¼ hours

2032, 2155 (4-11) W. Chaplin & Co. / W. Gilbert & Co.

'THE TANTIVY'

LONDON - HOUNSLOW - SLOUGH - MAIDENHEAD - HENLEY - OXFORD - WOODSTOCK -
SHIPSTON ON STOUR - STRATFORD UPON AVON - BIRMINGHAM (123 miles)

LONDON White Horse, Fetter Lane and

Blossoms Inn, Lawrence Lane   dep. 7 00 a.m.

BIRMINGHAM Hen & Chickens   dep. 8 00 a.m.

Journey time : 11¾ hours

2110, 2112 (4-8) W. Chaplin & Co.

'THE COURIER'

LONDON - HOUNSLOW - SLOUGH - MAIDENHEAD - HENLEY - OXFORD - WOODSTOCK -
SHIPSTON ON STOUR - STRATFORD UPON AVON - BIRMINGHAM (123 miles)

LONDON Spread Eagle, Gracechurch St. dep. 7 30 a.m.

BIRMINGHAM   dep.

Journey time: 13½ hours

2942, 2943 (4-11) W. Chaplin & Co. / E. Sherman & Co.

'THE UNION'

LONDON - EALING - UXBRIDGE - HIGH WYCOMBE - OXFORD - WOODSTOCK -
SHIPSTON ON STOUR - STRATFORD UPON AVON - BIRMINGHAM (119 miles)

LONDON Spread Eagle, Gracechurch St. and

Bull & Mouth, St. Martin's-le-Grand dep. 3 00 p.m.

BIRMINGHAM   dep. 3 30 p.m.

Journey time : 14 hours

3110, 3118 (4-11) J. Hearn & Co. / E. Sherman & Co.

LONDON - EDGWARE - STANMORE - WATFORD - HEMEL HEMPSTEAD - BERKHAMSTED -
TRING - AYLESBURY - BICESTER - BANBURY - WARWICK - SOLIHULL -
BIRMINGHAM (113 miles)

LONDON Kings Arms, Snow Hill and

Bull & Mouth, St. Martin's-le-Grand dep. 8 45 a.m.

BIRMINGHAM   dep.

Journey time : 14 hours

3462 (4-11), 3463 (4-8) W. Chaplin & Co.
'THE GREYHOUND'
LONDON - BARNET - ST. ALBANS - DUNSTABLE - FENNY STRATFORD – STONY STRATFORD - TOWCESTER - DAVENTRY - COVENTRY - BIRMINGHAM (109 miles).

LONDON Swan with Two Necks, Lad Lane dep. 6 30 p.m.
BIRMINGHAM, Albion   dep. 9 00 a.m.
Journey time : 12 hours

3466, 3501 (4-8) S.A. Mountain & Co. / W. Chaplin & Co.
'THE TALLY-HO'
LONDON - BARNET - ST. ALBANS - DUNSTABLE - FENNY STRATFORD – STONY STRATFORD - TOWCESTER - DAVENTRY - COVENTRY - BIRMINGHAM (109 miles).

LONDON Saracens Head, Snow Hill and
Swan with Two Necks, Lad Lane dep. 7 45 a.m.
BIRMINGHAM   dep. 8 00 a.m.
Journey time : 11 hours

3554, 3555 (4-11) B.W. Horne & Co.
'THE INDEPENDENT TALLY-HO'
LONDON - BARNET - ST. ALBANS - DUNSTABLE – FENNY STRATFORD - STONY STRATFORD - TOWCESTER - DAVENTRY - COVENTRY - BIRMINGHAM (111 miles).

LONDON Golden Cross, Charing Cross dep. 7 00 a.m.
BIRMINGHAM   dep. 8 00 a.m.
Journey time : 11¾ hours

3514, 3515 (4-8) J. Everett & Co.
'THE ECONOMIST'
LONDON - BARNET - ST. ALBANS - DUNSTABLE - FENNY STRATFORD - STONY STRATFORD - TOWCESTER - DAVENTRY - COVENTRY - BIRMINGHAM (109 miles).

LONDON George, Aldermanbury dep. 5 30 p.m.
BIRMINGHAM   dep. 5 30 p.m.
Journey time : 14 hours

4965 (6-12) W. Low & Co.
'THE TELEGRAPH'
LONDON – WOODFORD - EPPING - SAWBRIDGEWORTH - BISHOPS STORTFORD (30 miles)

LONDON Bull, Aldgate   dep. 2 45 p.m.
BISHOPS STORTFORD   dep. 6 00 a.m. Mon.
                                        8 00 a.m. Tues. to Sun.
Journey time : 4 hours

2059 (4-8) F. Rickards & Co.
'THE UNION'
LONDON - HOUNSLOW - STAINES - EGHAM - BAGSHOT - CAMBERLEY -
BLACKWATER (32½ miles).
> LONDON Bolt-in-Tun, Fleet Street dep. 3 00 p.m.
> BLACKWATER   dep. 8 00 a.m.
> Journey time : 5 hours

1336 (4-11) J. Eldridge

LONDON - CROYDON - PURLEY - CATERHAM - GODSTONE - BLETCHINGLEY (21¾ miles).
> LONDON Bull, Bishopsgate Street dep. 3 00 p.m.
> BLETCHINGLEY   dep. 7 30 a.m.
> Journey time : 3 hours

1450 (4-8) B.W. Horne & Co.
'THE COMET'
LONDON - MORDEN - EPSOM - LEATHERHEAD - DORKING - BILLINGSHURST -
PULBOROUGH - ARUNDEL - LITTLEHAMPTON - BOGNOR (66 miles).
> LONDON Golden Cross, Charing Cross dep. 9 00 a.m. Tu., Th., Sat.
> BOGNOR   dep. 9 00 a.m. Mon., Wed., Fri.
> Journey time : 8½ hours

3422, 3513 (4-11) J. Hearn & Co.
'THE PERSEVERANCE'
LONDON - BARNET - HATFIELD - STEVENAGE - BALDOCK - BIGGLESWADE -
EATON SOCON - ST. NEOTS - HUNTINGDON - NORMAN CROSS - PETERBOROUGH -
MARKET DEEPING - SPALDING - BOSTON (117 miles).
> LONDON Kings Arms, Snow Hill dep. 6 45 a.m. Tu., W., Th., Sat.
>   6 00 p.m. Mon., Fri.
> BOSTON Peacock and Red Lion   dep. 10 00 a.m. Mon. to Sat.
> Journey time : 13¾ hours

4964 (4-11) I. Alexander & Co.
'THE SOVEREIGN'
LONDON - ILFORD - ROMFORD - BRENTWOOD - CHELMSFORD - BRAINTREE (40 miles).
> LONDON Three Nuns, Aldgate dep. 3 00 p.m. Tues. to Sat.
>   4 00 p.m. Mon.
> BRAINTREE   dep. 5 00 a.m. Mon.
>   7 00 a.m. Tues. to Sat.
> Journey time : 5 hours

4919 (4-11) J. Murrells

LONDON - ILFORD - ROMFORD - BRENTWOOD (18 miles).
          LONDON The Bull, Aldgate dep.
          BRENTWOOD   dep.
             Journey time:

2116 (4-11) R. Fagg & Co.
              'THE SWIFTSURE'
LONDON - HOUNSLOW - STAINES - EGHAM - BAGSHOT - CAMBERLEY -
HARTLEY WINTNEY - BASINGSTOKE - WHITCHURCH - ANDOVER -
AMESBURY - WARMINSTER - FROME - SHEPTON MALLET - WELLS -
STREET - GLASTONBURY - BRIDGWATER (141 miles).
          LONDON Bell & Crown, Holborn dep. 6 45 a.m. Tu., Th., Sat.
          BRIDGWATER   dep.   Mon., Wed., Fri.
             Journey time: 15½ hours

1293, 1310 (4-8) W. Cripps & Co.
              'THE ALERT'
LONDON - SUTTON - REIGATE - CRAWLEY - HANDCROSS - HICKSTEAD -
BRIGHTON (55 miles).
          LONDON Yorkshire Stingo, Paddington dep. 8 00 a.m.
          BRIGHTON Hine's Office, 52 East Street dep. 9 00 a.m.
             Journey time: 6 hours

1330, 1331 (4-11) W. Cripps & Co.
             'THE EMERALD'
LONDON - CROYDON - PURLEY - REDHILL - HORLEY - CRAWLEY -
HANDCROSS - HICKSTEAD - BRIGHTON (55 miles).
          LONDON Yorkshire Stingo, Paddington dep. 9 00 a.m.
          BRIGHTON Capp's Office, 5 Castle Square dep. 10 00 a.m.
             Journey time: 6½ hours

1371, 1372 (4-11) W. Cripps & Co.
             'THE TELEGRAPH'
LONDON - SUTTON - REIGATE - CRAWLEY - HANDCROSS - HICKSTEAD -
BRIGHTON (55 miles).
          LONDON Yorkshire Stingo, Paddington dep.
          BRIGHTON Snow's Office, 3 Castle Square dep. 10 00 a.m.
             Journey time:

1328, 1329 (4-8) W. Bryant & Co.
'THE AGE'
LONDON – CROYDON – PURLEY – REDHILL – HORLEY – CRAWLEY –
HANDCROSS – HICKSTEAD – BRIGHTON (54 miles).

LONDON Portman Street   dep. 12 00 noon
BRIGHTON Red Office, 10 Castle Square dep. 12 00 noon
Journey time: $5\frac{1}{2}$ hours

1413, 1419 (4-8) W. Haines & Co.
'THE AGE'
LONDON – CROYDON – PURLEY – REDHILL – HORLEY – CRAWLEY –
HANDCROSS – HICKSTEAD – BRIGHTON (54 miles).

LONDON Baker Street   dep. 12 00 noon
BRIGHTON Capp's Office, 5 Castle Square dep. 12 00 noon
Journey time: $5\frac{1}{4}$ hours

1428, 1429 (11-4) G. Shillibeer
'THE DILIGENCE'
LONDON – SUTTON – REIGATE – HORLEY – POUND HILL – CUCKFIELD –
BRIGHTON (54 miles).

LONDON 336 Oxford Street dep. 10 30 a.m.
BRIGHTON Clarence Hotel   dep. 10 30 a.m.
Journey time: $6\frac{1}{4}$ hours

1350, 1351 (4-11) M. Sanderson & Co.
'THE ITEM'
LONDON – CROYDON – PURLEY – REDHILL – HORLEY – POUND HILL –
CUCKFIELD – BRIGHTON (52$\frac{1}{4}$ miles).

LONDON Boar & Castle, Oxford Street dep. 3 00 p.m.
BRIGHTON Blue Office, Castle Square dep. 6 00 a.m. Mon, Tu.
  8 00 a.m. Wed.–Sun.
Journey time: $5\frac{3}{4}$ hours

1352, 1353 (4-11) M. Sanderson & Co.
'THE TRUE BLUE'
LONDON – CROYDON – PURLEY – REDHILL – HORLEY – POUND HILL –
CUCKFIELD – BRIGHTON (52$\frac{1}{2}$ miles).

LONDON Boar & Castle, Oxford Street dep. 8 30 a.m.
BRIGHTON Blue Office, Castle Square dep. 10 00 a.m.
Journey time: $5\frac{1}{2}$ hours

1411, 1412 (4-11) J. Cripps & Co.
'THE ROYAL GEORGE'
LONDON – CROYDON - PURLEY - REDHILL - HORLEY - POUND HILL –
CUCKFIELD – BRIGHTON (53 miles).
> LONDON Boar & Castle, Oxford Street dep. 10 30 a.m.
> BRIGHTON Blue Office, Castle Square dep. 11 00 a.m.
> Journey time : 6 hours

1460, 1461 (4-12) B.W. Horne & Co.
'THE MAGNET'
LONDON - SUTTON - REIGATE - HORLEY - POUND HILL – CUCKFIELD -
BRIGHTON (53 miles).
> LONDON Gloster Warehouse, Oxford Street dep. 9 30 a.m.
> BRIGHTON Spread Eagle Office, 18 Castle Square dep. 11 00 a.m.
> Journey time: $5\frac{1}{4}$ hours

1462 (4-12) B.W. Horne & Co.
'THE TIMES'
LONDON - CROYDON - PURLEY - REDHILL - HORLEY - CRAWLEY - HANDCROSS -
HICKSTEAD - BRIGHTON (53 miles).
> LONDON Gloster Warehouse, Oxford Street dep. 7 45 a.m.
> BRIGHTON Red Office, 10 Castle Square dep. 5 00 p.m.
> Journey time: $5\frac{1}{2}$ hours

1345, 1346 (4-11) W. Gilbert & Co.
'THE TIMES'
LONDON – CROYDON – PURLEY - REDHILL - HORLEY - CRAWLEY - HANDCROSS -
HICKSTEAD - BRIGHTON (52 miles).
> LONDON The Bull, Holborn dep. 1 45 p.m.
> BRIGHTON Age Office, 5 Castle Sq. dep. 7 00 a.m.
> Journey time : $5\frac{1}{4}$ hours

1458, 1459 (4-12) B.W. Horne & Co.
'THE REGENT'
LONDON - CROYDON - PURLEY - REDHILL - HORLEY - CRAWLEY - HANDCROSS -
HICKSTEAD - BRIGHTON (53 miles).
> LONDON George & Blue Boar, Holborn dep. 9 45 a.m.
> BRIGHTON Red Office, 10 Castle Sq. dep. 10 00 a.m.
> Journey time : $5\frac{1}{2}$ hours

1347, 1348 (4-11) W. Gilbert & Co.
'THE UNION'
LONDON - SUTTON - REIGATE - CRAWLEY - HANDCROSS - HICKSTEAD - BRIGHTON (54 miles).
LONDON Price's, Islington   dep. 9 30 a.m.
BRIGHTON 134 North Street   dep. 11 00 a.m.
Journey time: $6\frac{1}{2}$ hours

1362 (4-11) W. Chaplin & Co.
'THE VIVID'
LONDON - CROYDON - PURLEY - REDHILL - HORLEY - CRAWLEY - HANDCROSS - HICKSTEAD - BRIGHTON (52 miles).
LONDON Spread Eagle, Gracechurch Street   dep. 6 00 a.m.
BRIGHTON Spread Eagle Office, 18 Castle Square dep. 2 45 p.m.
Journey time: $5\frac{1}{4}$ hours

1360 (4-12) W. Chaplin & Co.
'THE SOVEREIGN'
LONDON - CROYDON - PURLEY - REDHILL - HORLEY - CRAWLEY - HANDCROSS - HICKSTEAD - BRIGHTON (52 miles).
LONDON Spread Eagle, Gracechurch Street   dep. 7 45 a.m.
BRIGHTON Spread Eagle Office, 18 Castle Square dep. 3 00 p.m.
Journey time: 6 hours

1363, 1364 (4-11) W. Chaplin & Co.
'THE COMET'
LONDON - CROYDON - PURLEY - REDHILL - HORLEY - CRAWLEY - HANDCROSS - HICKSTEAD - BRIGHTON (52 miles).
LONDON Spread Eagle, Gracechurch Street   dep. 9 45 a.m.
BRIGHTON Spread Eagle Office, 18 Castle Square dep. 10 00 a.m.
Journey time: $5\frac{1}{4}$ hours

1424, 1425 (4-11) J. Nelson & Co.
'THE NEW DART'
LONDON - SUTTON - REIGATE - CRAWLEY - HANDCROSS - HICKSTEAD - BRIGHTON (53 miles).
LONDON The Bull, Aldgate   dep. 9 45 a.m.
BRIGHTON Snow's Office, 3 Castle Square dep. 12 00 noon
Journey time $5\frac{1}{2}$ hours

1979, 2050 (4-11) E. Sherman & Co. / B.W. Horne & Co.
'THE REGULATOR'
LONDON - HOUNSLOW - SLOUGH - MAIDENHEAD - READING - NEWBURY - HUNGERFORD - MARLBOROUGH - CALNE - CHIPPENHAM - BATH - BRISTOL (122 miles).

LONDON Bull & Mouth, St. Martin's-le-Grand dep. 6 30 a.m.
BRISTOL White Hart and White Lion dep. 7 00 a.m.
Journey time: 13 hours

2011, 2012 (6-12) H. Dibbin & Co.
'THE GENERAL STAGE COACH COMPANY'S NIGHT COACH'
LONDON - HOUNSLOW - SLOUGH - MAIDENHEAD - READING - NEWBURY - HUNGERFORD - MARLBOROUGH - CALNE - CHIPPENHAM - BATH - BRISTOL (122 miles).

LONDON Gerrard's Hall, Basing Lane dep. 2 30 p.m.
BRISTOL Rummer Hotel, GSCC Office dep. 1 00 p.m.
Journey time: 18 hours

2014, 2148 (4-11) M. Fromont & Co.
'THE GENERAL STAGE COACH COMPANY'S DAY COACH'
LONDON - HOUNSLOW - SLOUGH - MAIDENHEAD - READING - NEWBURY - HUNGERFORD - MARLBOROUGH - CALNE - CHIPPENHAM - BATH - BRISTOL (122 miles).

LONDON Blossoms Inn, Lawrence Lane dep. 6 00 a.m.
BRISTOL Rummer Hotel, GSCC Office dep. 6 30 a.m.
Journey time: 14 hours

2089, 2090 (4-11) J. Niblett & Co.
'THE MONARCH'
LONDON - HOUNSLOW - SLOUGH - MAIDENHEAD - READING - NEWBURY - HUNGERFORD - MARLBOROUGH - CALNE - CHIPPENHAM - BATH - BRISTOL (122 miles).

LONDON Belle Sauvage, Ludgate Hill dep. 4 30 p.m.
BRISTOL White Hart and White Lion dep. 5 15 p.m.
Journey time: 15 hours

2134, 2135 (4-8) S. A. Mountain & Co.
'THE AGE'
LONDON - HOUNSLOW - SLOUGH - MAIDENHEAD - READING - NEWBURY - HUNGERFORD - MARLBOROUGH - CALNE - CHIPPENHAM - BATH - BRISTOL (123 miles).

LONDON White Bear, Basinghall Street dep. 3 30 p.m.
BRISTOL The Bush, Corn Street dep. 2 30 p.m.
Journey time: 15½ hours

12

2108, 2144 (4-11) W. Chaplin & Co.
'THE EMERALD'
LONDON-HOUNSLOW-SLOUGH-MAIDENHEAD-READING-NEWBURY-HUNGERFORD-
MARLBOROUGH-DEVIZES-MELKSHAM-BATH-BRISTOL (123 miles).
LONDON Spread Eagle, Gracechurch Street dep. 7 00 a.m.
BRISTOL White Lion, Broad Street   dep. 7 45 a.m.
Journey time : 13¾ hours

2160, 2161 (4-11) W. Chaplin & Co.
'COOPER'S COMPANY'S NIGHT COACH'
LONDON-HOUNSLOW-SLOUGH-MAIDENHEAD-READING-NEWBURY-HUNGERFORD-
MARLBOROUGH-DEVIZES-MELKSHAM-BATH-BRISTOL (123 miles).
LONDON Swan with Two Necks, Lad Lane   dep. 5 00 p.m.
BRISTOL Cooper's Office, 6 High Street   dep. 5 30 p.m.
Journey time : 13½ hours

2142, 2189 (4-11) W. Chaplin & Co.
'COOPER'S COMPANY'S DAY COACH'
LONDON-HOUNSLOW-SLOUGH-MAIDENHEAD-READING-NEWBURY-HUNGERFORD-
MARLBOROUGH-CALNE-CHIPPENHAM-BATH-BRISTOL (122 miles).
LONDON Swan with Two Necks, Lad Lane   dep. 7 00 a.m.
BRISTOL Cooper's Office, 6 High Street dep. 7 45 a.m.
Journey time : 13 hours

2226, 2227 (4-11) B. W. Horne & Co.
'THE REGULATOR'
LONDON-HOUNSLOW-SLOUGH-MAIDENHEAD-READING-NEWBURY-HUNGERFORD-
MARLBOROUGH-DEVIZES-MELKSHAM-BATH-BRISTOL (123 miles).
LONDON Cross Keys, Wood Street   dep. 6 30 p.m.
BRISTOL White Lion, Broad Street   dep. 4 00 p.m.
Journey time : 15 hours

485 (4-11) J. Edwards & Co.
'THE NELSON'
LONDON-DARTFORD-STROOD-ROCHESTER-CHATHAM-BROMPTON
(31 miles).
LONDON Spread Eagle, Gracechurch Street dep. 5 00 p.m.
BROMPTON   dep. 5 30 a.m. Mon.
                                  7 00 a.m. Tu.-Sat.
Journey time: 3¾ hours

486 (4-11) J. Edwards & Co.
'THE COMMODORE'
LONDON-DARTFORD-STROOD-ROCHESTER-CHATHAM-BROMPTON ($32\frac{1}{2}$ miles).

      LONDON Golden Cross, Charing Cross dep. 2 00 p.m.
      BROMPTON   dep. 9 30 a.m.
          Journey time: $3\frac{1}{2}$ hours

4359 (4-11) W. Kay

LONDON - WALTHAM CROSS - CHESHUNT - BROXBOURNE (16 miles).

      LONDON The Vine, Bishopsgate Street dep. 4 30 p.m.
      BROXBOURNE   dep.
          Journey time:

2930 (4-11) W. Tollitt

LONDON - EALING - UXBRIDGE - IVER HEATH - STOKE POGES - FARNHAM ROYAL - BURNHAM (26 miles)

      LONDON The Bull, Holborn   dep. 2 30 p.m.
      BURNHAM   dep.
          Journey time:

4958, 4959 (4-11) W. Chaplin & Co.
'THE OLD BURY'
LONDON - ILFORD - ROMFORD - BRENTWOOD - CHELMSFORD - BRAINTREE - HALSTEAD - SUDBURY - LONG MELFORD - BURY ST. EDMUNDS (74 miles).

      LONDON Spread Eagle Office, Piccadilly dep. 8 30 a.m.
      BURY ST. EDMUNDS   dep. 9 30 a.m.
          Journey time: 9 hours

4756, 4757 (4-11) B.W. Horne
'THE MARQUIS OF CORNWALLIS'
LONDON - WOODFORD - EPPING - SAWBRIDGEWORTH - BISHOPS STORTFORD - GREAT CHESTERFORD - NEWMARKET - BURY ST. EDMUNDS (77 miles).

      LONDON Golden Cross, Charing Cross dep. 8 30 a.m.
      BURY ST. EDMUNDS   dep. 9 30 a.m.
          Journey time: 9 hours

3116 (4-8) M. Sanderson & Co.

LONDON – EDGWARE – STANMORE – BUSHEY HEATH (13½ miles).
> LONDON Blue Posts, Holborn   dep. 4 00 p.m.
> BUSHEY HEATH   dep.
> Journey time: 1¾ hours

3521, 3522 (4-11) W. Chaplin & Co.
'THE TELEGRAPH'
LONDON – WALTHAM CROSS – HODDESDON – WARE – PUCKERIDGE –
BARKWAY – BARLEY – FOWLMERE – CAMBRIDGE (53 miles).
> LONDON White Horse, Fetter Lane dep. 10 00 a.m.
> CAMBRIDGE   dep. 10 00 a.m.
> Journey time: 6 hours

4360, 4361 (4-11) W. Chaplin & Co.
'THE ROCKET'
LONDON – WALTHAM CROSS – HODDESDON – WARE – PUCKERIDGE –
BUNTINGFORD – ROYSTON – CAMBRIDGE (54 miles).
> LONDON White Horse Cellar, Piccadilly dep. 1 30 p.m.
> CAMBRIDGE   dep. 3 00 p.m.
> Journey time: 6 hours

4341 (4-5) W. Wilkins & Co.
'THE BEEHIVE'
LONDON – WALTHAM CROSS – HODDESDON – WARE – PUCKERIDGE –
BUNTINGFORD – ROYSTON – CAMBRIDGE (54 miles).
> LONDON Three Nuns, Aldgate dep. 11 45 a.m. Tu., Th., Sat.
> CAMBRIDGE   dep. 9 00 a.m. Mon., Wed, Fri.
> Journey time: 5¾ hours

4411 (4-11) W. Eken & Co.
'THE STAR'
LONDON – WALTHAM CROSS – HODDESDON – WARE – PUCKERIDGE –
BUNTINGFORD – ROYSTON – CAMBRIDGE (52 miles).
> LONDON Belle Sauvage, Ludgate Hill dep. 3 45 p.m.
> CAMBRIDGE   dep. 7 00 a.m.
> Journey time: 6 hours

4751, 4752 (4-11) B.W. Horne & Co.

'THE FLY'

LONDON-WOODFORD-EPPING-SAWBRIDGEWORTH - BISHOPS
STORTFORD-GREAT CHESTERFORD-CAMBRIDGE (60 miles).

LONDON Green Man & Still, Oxford Street dep. 9 30a.m.
CAMBRIDGE   dep. 10 00a.m.

Journey time : 7 hours

4753 (4-11) B.W. Horne & Co.

'THE TIMES'

LONDON - WOODFORD- EPPING- SAWBRIDGEWORTH- BISHOPS
STORTFORD-GREAT CHESTERFORD-CAMBRIDGE (58 miles).

LONDON George & Blue Boar, Holborn dep. 3 00p.m.
CAMBRIDGE   dep. 6 00 a.m. Mon.
            7 00 a.m. Tu.- Sat.

Journey time :

491, 492, 493, 494 (4-11) J. Edwards & Co.

'THE EAGLE'

LONDON - DARTFORD -STROOD-ROCHESTER - CHATHAM -
SITTINGBOURNE - OSPRINGE-CANTERBURY (55 miles).

LONDON Spread Eagle, Gracechurch Street dep. 8 30a.m., 7 30p.m.
CANTERBURY   dep. 10 00a.m., 9 00p.m.

Journey time : 8 hours

489, 490 (4-11) J. Edwards & Co.

'THE TALLY - HO'

LONDON - DARTFORD- STROOD- ROCHESTER- CHATHAM-
SITTINGBOURNE - OSPRINGE- CANTERBURY (55 miles).

LONDON Spread Eagle, Gracechurch Street dep. 3 00p.m.
CANTERBURY   dep. 3 30p.m.

Journey time : 7 hours

483, 507 (4-11) S.A. Mountain & Co./ B.W. Horne & Co.

'THE DEFIANCE'

LONDON -DARTFORD-STROOD- ROCHESTER - CHATHAM-
SITTINGBOURNE- OSPRINGE -CANTERBURY (58 miles).

LONDON Regent Circus, Piccadilly   dep. 6 00p.m.
CANTERBURY   dep. 9 00 p.m.

Journey time : 9 hours

604 (4-5) J. Edwards & Co.

LONDON - DARTFORD - STROOD - ROCHESTER - CHATHAM - SITTINGBOURNE - OSPRINGE - CANTERBURY (55 miles).

    LONDON Spread Eagle, Gracechurch Street dep. (§)
    CANTERBURY   dep. (§)
        Journey time :
§ - 3 journeys weekly.

534 (6-3) W. Peall

      Omnibus : 'THE HOPE'

LONDON - DARTFORD - STROOD - ROCHESTER - CHATHAM (31 miles).

    LONDON Saracens Head, Friday Street dep. 3 00 p.m. Tu., Th., Sat.
    CHATHAM   dep. 9 00 a.m. Mon., Wed., Fri.
      Journey time : $7\frac{3}{4}$ hours

4914, 4915 (6-12) W. Woods

LONDON - ILFORD - ROMFORD - BRENTWOOD - CHELMSFORD (29 miles)
    LONDON Spread Eagle, Gracechurch Street dep. 9 45 a.m., 3 45 p.m.
    CHELMSFORD   dep.
      Journey time : $3\frac{1}{2}$ hours

2052, 2053 (4-11) R. Nelson & Co.
      'THE BERKELEY HUNT'
LONDON - EALING - UXBRIDGE - HIGH WYCOMBE - OXFORD - WITNEY - CHELTENHAM (100 miles).

    LONDON Belle Sauvage, Ludgate Hill dep. 7 30 a.m.
    CHELTENHAM   dep.
      Journey time : 11 hours

2107, 2222 (4-11) W. Chaplin & Co./ B.W. Horne & Co.
      'THE MAGNET'

LONDON - HOUNSLOW - SLOUGH - MAIDENHEAD - HENLEY - OXFORD - WITNEY - CHELTENHAM (101 miles).
    LONDON Spread Eagle, Gracechurch Street dep. 7 00 a.m.
      Cross Keys, Wood Street   dep. 7 15 a.m.
    CHELTENHAM   dep. 7 45 a.m.
      Journey time : 11 hours

2024, 2028 (4-8) R. Gray & Co.

LONDON - KINGSTON - SUNBURY - SHEPPERTON - CHERTSEY (23 miles).

    LONDON Bolt-in-Tun, Fleet Street dep. 8 30 a.m., 3 00 p.m.
    CHERTSEY   dep.

    Journey time: 3 hours

2029 (4-8) R. Gray & Co.

LONDON - HOUNSLOW - FELTHAM - LALEHAM - CHERTSEY (22 miles).

    LONDON Bolt-in-Tun, Fleet Street dep. 4 30 p.m.
    CHERTSEY   dep.

    Journey time: 2½ hours

3115 (6-12) W. Wyatt & Co.

LONDON - EDGWARE - STANMORE - WATFORD - RICKMANSWORTH - CHESHAM (29 miles).

    LONDON The Bull, Holborn dep. 3 00 p.m.
    CHESHAM   dep. 8 00 a.m.

    Journey time: 4½ hours

2027, 2225 (4-11) B.W. Horne & Co./R. Gray & Co.

    'THE DUKE OF RICHMOND'

LONDON - KINGSTON - ESHER - GUILDFORD - GODALMING - MOUSEHILL - PETWORTH/MIDHURST - CHICHESTER (62/65 miles).

    LONDON Cross Keys, Wood Street and
        Bolt-in-Tun, Fleet Street dep. 8 30 a.m. (A)
    CHICHESTER   dep. 9 00 a.m. (B)

    Journey time: 8/8½ hours

A - Via Petworth on Mon., Wed., Fri., via Midhurst on Tu., Th., Sat.
B - Via Midhurst on Mon., Wed., Fri., via Petworth on Tu., Th., Sat.

2099 (4-11) J. Cross & Co.

    'THE INDEPENDENT'

LONDON - KINGSTON - ESHER - GUILDFORD - GODALMING - MOUSEHILL - MIDHURST - CHICHESTER (63 miles).

    LONDON Belle Sauvage, Ludgate Hill dep. 7 30 a.m. Mon., Wed., Fri.
    CHICHESTER   dep. 9 00 a.m. Tu., Th., Sat.

    Journey time: 8 hours

4952 (4-11) E. Deacon & Co.

'THE FLY'

LONDON - ILFORD - ROMFORD - BRENTWOOD - CHELMSFORD - COGGESHALL (44 miles).

LONDON Saracens Head, Aldgate dep. 2 00 p.m.
COGGESHALL dep. 9 00 a.m.

Journey time: $4\frac{1}{2}$ hours

4962, 4987 (4-11) R. Nelson & Co.

'THE DEFIANCE'

LONDON - ILFORD - ROMFORD - BRENTWOOD - CHELMSFORD - COLCHESTER (52 miles).

LONDON Belle Sauvage, Ludgate Hill dep. 2 30 p.m.
COLCHESTER dep. 1 45 p.m.

Journey time: $5\frac{3}{4}$ hours

4960, 4961 (4-11) W. Chaplin & Co.

'THE WELLINGTON'

LONDON - ILFORD - ROMFORD - BRENTWOOD - CHELMSFORD - COLCHESTER (53 miles).

LONDON Spread Eagle Office, Piccadilly dep. 8 30 a.m.
COLCHESTER dep. 9 00 a.m.

Journey time: $6\frac{1}{2}$ hours

---

498 (8-4) J. Stoneham

LONDON - DARTFORD (15 miles).

LONDON Union Office, 11 Gracechurch Street dep. 4 30 p.m.
DARTFORD dep.

Journey time: 3 hours

---

545 (8-4) T. Finniss

LONDON - DARTFORD (15 miles).

LONDON George & Gate, Gracechurch Street dep. 5 00 p.m.
DARTFORD dep.

Journey time: 3 hours

---

482 (4-11) C. Huggett

'THE DART'

LONDON - DARTFORD (15 miles).

LONDON Eastcheap dep. 4 00 p.m.
DARTFORD dep. 7 45 a.m.

Journey time: 2 hours

3436 (4-11) W. Smith

'THE DAVENTRY ACCOMMODATION COACH'

LONDON - BARNET - ST. ALBANS - DUNSTABLE — FENNY STRATFORD -
STONY STRATFORD - TOWCESTER - DAVENTRY (72 miles).

LONDON Three Cups, Aldersgate Street dep. 7 30 a.m. Tu., Th., Sat.
DAVENTRY   dep. 7 00 a.m. Mon., Wed., Fri.

Journey time : 12 hours

1279 (6-12) W. Broad

LONDON - MORDEN - EPSOM - LEATHERHEAD - DORKING (24 miles).

LONDON Spread Eagle, Gracechurch Street dep. 4 00 p.m.
DORKING   dep. 7 00 a.m.

Journey time : 4 hours

1452 (4-11) B.W. Horne & Co.

LONDON - MORDEN - EPSOM - LEATHERHEAD - DORKING (24 miles).

LONDON Golden Cross, Charing Cross   dep. 8 30 a.m.
DORKING   dep. 4 00 p.m. Mon. to Sat.
                                                       5 00 p.m. Sun.

Journey time : 3 hours

1335 (6-12) M. Holden

LONDON - MORDEN - EPSOM - LEATHERHEAD - DORKING (25 miles).

LONDON Golden Cross, Charing Cross   dep. 2 45 p.m.
DORKING   dep. 9 00 a.m.

Journey time : 4 hours

**452, 472, 502, 503, 504, 506 (4-11) R. Fagg & Co./ W. Gilbert & Co./
R. Gray & Co./ B.W. Horne & Co./ E. Sherman & Co./ J. Nelson & Co.**

'THE UNION'

LONDON - DARTFORD - STROOD - ROCHESTER - CHATHAM -
SITTINGBOURNE - OSPRINGE - CANTERBURY - DOVER (72 miles).

LONDON White Bear, Piccadilly dep. 8 30 a.m., 10 30 a.m., 6 30 p.m.
DOVER   dep. 6 00 a.m., 8 00 a.m., 6 00 p.m.

Journey time : $9\frac{1}{2}$ hours (day coaches)
$10\frac{1}{2}$ hours (night coaches)

470, 471 (4-11) E. Sherman & Co.

'THE PHOENIX'

LONDON - DARTFORD - STROOD - ROCHESTER - CHATHAM - SITTINGBOURNE -
OSPRINGE - CANTERBURY - DOVER (73 miles).

LONDON Green Man & Still, Oxford Street dep. 9 00 a.m.
DOVER   dep. 9 00 a.m.

Journey time : 9 hours

495, 496 (4-11) J. Edwards & Co.

'THE TELEGRAPH'

LONDON - DARTFORD - STROOD - ROCHESTER - CHATHAM - SITTINGBOURNE -
OSPRINGE - CANTERBURY - DOVER (73 miles).

LONDON Gloster Warehouse, Oxford Street dep. 7 45 a.m.
DOVER   dep. 7 45 a.m.

Journey time : 8½ hours

613, 614 (4-11) B. W. Horne & Co.

'THE EXPRESS'

LONDON - DARTFORD - STROOD - ROCHESTER - CHATHAM - SITTINGBOURNE -
OSPRINGE - CANTERBURY - DOVER (73 miles).

LONDON Old Bell, Holborn   dep. 7 00 a.m.
DOVER   dep. 6 30 a.m.

Journey time : 10 hours

4940, 4941 (4-11) J. Nelson & Co.

'THE TIMES'

LONDON - CHIGWELL - ONGAR - LEADEN RODING - DUNMOW (35 miles).

LONDON The Bull, Aldgate   dep. 10 00 a.m.
DUNMOW   dep. 11 30 a.m.

Journey time : 4¼ hours

1457 (4-11) B. W. Horne & Co.

'THE EASTBOURNE SAFETY COACH'

LONDON - CROYDON - PURLEY - CATERHAM - GODSTONE - EAST GRINSTEAD -
FOREST ROW - UCKFIELD - EAST HOATHLY - HAILSHAM - EASTBOURNE
(65 miles).

LONDON George & Blue Boar, Holborn dep. 8 00 a.m. Tu, Th, Sat.
EASTBOURNE   dep. 8 00 a.m. Mon, Wed, Fri.

Journey time :

2001 (4-8) B.W. Horne & Co.

LONDON - HOUNSLOW - STAINES – EGHAM - ENGLEFIELD GREEN
(22 miles).

> LONDON Old Bell, Holborn   dep. 3 00 p.m.
> ENGLEFIELD GREEN   dep. 8 00 a.m.
>
> Journey time: 3½ hours

5007 (6-12) P. Barnard & Co.

'THE EPPING COACH'

LONDON – WOODFORD - EPPING (17 miles).

> LONDON Three Nuns, Aldgate   dep. 4 00 p.m.
> EPPING   dep. 7 00 a.m. Mon.
>   8 30 a.m. Tu.—Sun.
>
> Journey time: 2½ hours

1405 (4-8) W. Broad & Co.

LONDON - MORDEN - EPSOM (17 miles).

> LONDON The Bull, Holborn   dep. 3 30 p.m.
> EPSOM   dep.
>
> Journey time: 2½ hours

2212 (4-8) R. Gray & Co.

LONDON - KINGSTON - ESHER (16 miles).

> LONDON Bolt-in-Tun, Fleet Street dep. 3 30 p.m.
> ESHER   dep. 9 00 a.m.
>
> Journey time: 2½ hours

1995, 1996, 1997 (4-8) J. Nelson & Co./E. Sherman & Co.

'THE TELEGRAPH'

LONDON - HOUNSLOW - STAINES - EGHAM – BAGSHOT - CAMBERLEY -
HARTLEY WINTNEY - BASINGSTOKE - WHITCHURCH - ANDOVER - AMESBURY -
MERE - WINCANTON - ILCHESTER - ILMINSTER - HONITON - EXETER (168 miles).

> LONDON The Bull, Aldgate   dep. 4 30 a.m.
> Bull & Mouth, St. Martin's-le-Grand dep. 5 00 a.m.
> EXETER   dep.
>
> Journey time: 18 hours

1993, 2143 (4-8) J. Nelson & Co./E. Sherman & Co.

'THE DEFIANCE'

LONDON - HOUNSLOW - STAINES - EGHAM - BAGSHOT - CAMBERLEY -
HARTLEY WINTNEY - BASINGSTOKE - WHITCHURCH - ANDOVER - AMESBURY -
MERE - WINCANTON - ILCHESTER - ILMINSTER - HONITON - EXETER (168 miles).

LONDON	The Bull, Aldgate	dep. 3 15 p.m.
	Bull & Mouth, St. Martin's-le-Grand	dep. 3 45 p.m.
EXETER		dep. 5 00 p.m.

Journey time: 19 hours

2046, 2047, 2048 (4-11) E. Sherman & Co.

'THE EXETER SUBSCRIPTION COACH'

LONDON - HOUNSLOW - STAINES - EGHAM - BAGSHOT - CAMBERLEY -
HARTLEY WINTNEY - BASINGSTOKE - WHITCHURCH - ANDOVER - AMESBURY -
MERE - WINCANTON - ILCHESTER - ILMINSTER - HONITON - EXETER (168 miles).

LONDON	Bull & Mouth, St. Martin's-le-Grand	dep. 4 00 p.m.
EXETER		dep. 4 00 p.m.

Journey time: 19 hours

1977, 2193, 2207 (6-12) R. Fagg & Co.

'THE TRAVELLER'

LONDON - HOUNSLOW - STAINES - EGHAM - BAGSHOT - CAMBERLEY -
HARTLEY WINTNEY - BASINGSTOKE - STOCKBRIDGE - SALISBURY - SHAFTESBURY -
SHERBORNE - YEOVIL - CREWKERNE - CHARD - HONITON - EXETER
(175 miles).

LONDON	Bell & Crown, Holborn	dep. 6 45 p.m.
EXETER		dep.

Journey time: 25 hours

2113, 2131, 2206 (4-8) W. Chaplin & Co./S. A. Mountain & Co.

'THE HERALD'

LONDON - HOUNSLOW - STAINES - EGHAM - BAGSHOT - CAMBERLEY -
HARTLEY WINTNEY - BASINGSTOKE - STOCKBRIDGE - SALISBURY - SHAFTESBURY -
SHERBORNE - YEOVIL - CREWKERNE - CHARD - HONITON - EXETER
(175 miles).

LONDON	Swan with Two Necks, Lad Lane and Saracens Head, Snow Hill	dep. 6 00 a.m.
EXETER		dep.

Journey time: 23 hours

2228 (4-11) B. W. Horne & Co.

LONDON - HOUNSLOW - SLOUGH - MAIDENHEAD - HENLEY - ABINGDON -
FARINGDON (72 miles).

LONDON	Old Bell, Holborn	dep. 7 30 a.m. Mon., Wed., Fri.
FARINGDON		dep. Tu., Th., Sat.

Journey time: 9 hours

488, 508 (4-5) J.Edwards & Co./W.Gilbert & Co.

'THE TANTIVY'

LONDON - DARTFORD - STROOD - ROCHESTER - CHATHAM - SITTINGBOURNE - OSPRINGE - FAVERSHAM (47 miles).

LONDON Spread Eagle, Gracechurch Street
and Blossoms Inn, Lawrence Lane   dep. 12 00 noon
FAVERSHAM   dep. 9 45 a.m.

Journey time: 6 hours

510, 511 (4-11) W.Gilbert & Co.

'THE TIMES'

LONDON - SIDCUP - FARNINGHAM - WROTHAM - MAIDSTONE - CHARING - ASHFORD - HYTHE - FOLKESTONE (70 miles).

LONDON Blossoms Inn, Lawrence Lane   dep. 8 00 a.m.
FOLKESTONE   dep. 8 00 a.m.

Journey time: 8½ hours

2924, 2967 (4-11) R.Gray & Co./R.Fagg & Co.

'THE REGULATOR'

LONDON - EALING - UXBRIDGE - HIGH WYCOMBE - OXFORD - WITNEY - CHELTENHAM - GLOUCESTER (106 miles).

LONDON Bolt-in-Tun, Fleet Street
and Bell & Crown, Holborn   dep. 7 00 a.m.
GLOUCESTER   dep. 7 00 a.m.

Journey time: 12 hours

2937, 2963 (4-11) W.Chaplin & Co./W.Gilbert & Co.

'THE RETALIATOR'

LONDON - EALING - UXBRIDGE - HIGH WYCOMBE - OXFORD - WITNEY - CHELTENHAM - GLOUCESTER (106 miles).

LONDON Spread Eagle, Gracechurch Street
and Blossoms Inn, Lawrence Lane   dep. 7 00 a.m.
GLOUCESTER   dep.

Journey time: 11 hours

1803 (4-11) R.Gray & Co.

LONDON - KINGSTON - ESHER - GUILDFORD - GODALMING (36 miles).

LONDON Bolt-in-Tun, Fleet Street   dep. 2 30 p.m.
GODALMING   dep. 6 00 a.m. Mon.
8 00 a.m. Tu.-Sat.

Journey time: 5 hours

2104, 2105 (4-11) W. Chaplin & Co.
'THE EXPRESS'
LONDON - KINGSTON - ESHER - GUILDFORD - FARNHAM - ALTON - FAREHAM - GOSPORT (81 miles).

LONDON Spread Eagle, Gracechurch Street dep. 7 45 a.m.
GOSPORT dep. 8 00 a.m.
Journey time: 10 hours

423 (4-5) W. Newman
'THE SONS OF COMMERCE'
LONDON - DARTFORD - GRAVESEND (22 miles).

LONDON The Bull, Leadenhall Street dep. 8 00 a.m.
GRAVESEND dep. 4 30 p.m.
Journey time: 3½ hours

2034 (4-11) C. Faulkner
'THE UNION'
LONDON - KINGSTON - ESHER - GUILDFORD (30 miles).

LONDON Spread Eagle, Gracechurch Street dep. 3 30 p.m.
GUILDFORD dep. 7 00 a.m.
Journey time: 4 hours

1451 (4-11) B.W. Horne & Co.
'THE TIMES'
LONDON - MORDEN - EPSOM - LEATHERHEAD - GUILDFORD (31 miles).
LONDON Golden Cross, Charing Cross dep. 3 30 p.m.
GUILDFORD dep. 8 00 a.m.
Journey time: 4 hours

3457, 3459, 3517 (4-11) E. Sherman & Co.
'THE HOPE'
LONDON - BARNET - ST. ALBANS - DUNSTABLE - WOBURN - NEWPORT PAGNELL - NORTHAMPTON - MARKET HARBOROUGH - LEICESTER - LOUGHBOROUGH - NOTTINGHAM - MANSFIELD - CHESTERFIELD - SHEFFIELD - HUDDERSFIELD - HALIFAX (196 miles).

LONDON Bull & Mouth, St. Martin's-le-Grand dep. 5 45 p.m.
HALIFAX dep. 8 00 a.m.
Journey time: 23½ hours

4943 (4-8) J. Nelson & Co.

LONDON – WOODFORD – EPPING – HARLOW (23 miles).
      LONDON The Bull, Aldgate   dep. 3 30p.m.
      HARLOW   dep. 8 00 a.m.
          Journey time: 3 hours

577 (3-3), 578 (6-6) R. Shepherd & Co.
      'THE ROYAL BLUE COACH VAN'
LONDON – BROMLEY – FARNBOROUGH – SEVENOAKS – TONBRIDGE –
LAMBERHURST – ROBERTSBRIDGE – BATTLE – HASTINGS (65 miles).
      LONDON Shepherd's Warehouse, Camomile Street dep. 4 00p.m.
      HASTINGS   dep.
          Journey time: 12 hours

499, 500 (4-11) J. Breeds & Co.
      'THE PARAGON'
LONDON – BROMLEY – FARNBOROUGH – SEVENOAKS – TONBRIDGE –
TUNBRIDGE WELLS – WADHURST – ROBERTSBRIDGE – BATTLE –
HASTINGS (66 miles).
      LONDON Belle Sauvage, Ludgate Hill dep. 9 00a.m.
      HASTINGS   dep. 10 00 a.m.
          Journey time: 9 hours

477, 478 (4-11) R. Gray & Co./W. Chaplin & Co.
      'THE REGULATOR'
LONDON – BROMLEY – FARNBOROUGH – SEVENOAKS – TONBRIDGE –
LAMBERHURST – ROBERTSBRIDGE – BATTLE – HASTINGS (67 miles).
      LONDON White Horse Cellar, Piccadilly dep. 9 30a.m.
      HASTINGS   dep. 9 00a.m.
          Journey time: 9½ hours

551, 552 (4-11) B.W. Horne & Co.
      'THE EXPRESS'
LONDON – BROMLEY – FARNBOROUGH – SEVENOAKS – TONBRIDGE –
LAMBERHURST – ROBERTSBRIDGE – BATTLE – HASTINGS (68 miles).
      LONDON Golden Cross, Charing Cross dep. 8 30 a.m.
      HASTINGS   dep. 9 00a.m.
          Journey time: 7½ hours

546, 547 (4-11) B. W. Horne & Co.

'THE DESPATCH'

LONDON - BROMLEY - FARNBOROUGH - SEVENOAKS - TONBRIDGE - LAMBERHURST - ROBERTSBRIDGE - BATTLE - HASTINGS (67 miles).

LONDON George & Blue Boar, Holborn dep. 12 00 noon
HASTINGS dep. 10 30 a.m.

Journey time: 8½ hours

3447 (4-11) J. Scarborough

'THE SOVEREIGN'

LONDON - BARNET - HATFIELD (20½ miles).

LONDON Boar & Castle, Oxford Street dep. 3 30 p.m.
HATFIELD dep. 8 00 a.m.

Journey time: 3 hours

4988 (4-11) J. Tredgett & Co.

'THE TELEGRAPH'

LONDON - WOODFORD - EPPING - SAWBRIDGEWORTH - BISHOPS STORTFORD - SAFFRON WALDEN - HAVERHILL (56 miles).

LONDON Belle Sauvage, Ludgate Hill dep. 10 00 a.m. Tu., Th., Sat.
HAVERHILL dep. 8 30 a.m. Mon., Wed., Fri.

Journey time: 7¼ hours

3114 (6-12) J. Hearn & Co.

'THE PILOT'

LONDON - EDGWARE - STANMORE - WATFORD - HEMEL HEMPSTEAD (25 miles).

LONDON Kings Arms, Snow Hill dep. 3 30 p.m.
HEMEL HEMPSTEAD dep. 8 00 a.m.

Journey time: 3½ hours

3117 (6-12) W. Wyatt & Co.

'RODWAY'S COACH'

LONDON - EDGWARE - STANMORE - WATFORD - HEMEL HEMPSTEAD (25 miles).

LONDON The Bull, Holborn dep. 8 00 a.m.
HEMEL HEMPSTEAD dep. 4 00 p.m.

Journey time: 3½ hours

1990 (4-11), 1991 (4-8) J. Dixon & Co.

LONDON - HOUNSLOW - SLOUGH - MAIDENHEAD - HENLEY (37 miles).

LONDON Black Lion, Water Lane dep. 8 00 a.m., 2 30 p.m.
HENLEY dep. 8 00 a.m., 2 30 p.m.

Journey time: 4½ hours

2928, 2960 (4-8) R. Gray & Co.

'THE CHAMPION'

LONDON - EALING - UXBRIDGE - HIGH WYCOMBE - OXFORD -
WITNEY - CHELTENHAM - GLOUCESTER - NEWENT - HEREFORD
(138 miles).

LONDON Bolt-in-Tun, Fleet Street dep. 4 00 p.m.
HEREFORD   dep.

Journey time: 20 hours

1982, 1983 (4-11) R. Gray & Co./E. Sherman & Co.

'THE MAZEPPA'

LONDON - HOUNSLOW - SLOUGH - MAIDENHEAD - HENLEY -
OXFORD - WITNEY - CHELTENHAM - GLOUCESTER - NEWENT -
HEREFORD (142 miles).

LONDON Bolt-in-Tun, Fleet Street and
      Bull & Mouth, St. Martin's-le-Grand dep. 6 00 a.m.
HEREFORD   dep.

Journey time: 17 hours

3405 (4-11) A. Glenny & Co.

'THE ECLIPSE'

LONDON - BARNET - ESSENDON - HERTFORD (25 miles).

LONDON Boar & Castle, Oxford Street dep. 3 00 p.m.
HERTFORD   dep. 8 00 p.m.

Journey time: 3½ hours

4332 (4-8) M. Sanderson

'THE EXPRESS'

LONDON - WALTHAM CROSS - HODDESDON - WARE - HERTFORD
(24 miles).

LONDON Boar & Castle, Oxford Street dep. 7 00 a.m.
HERTFORD   dep. 3 00 p.m.

Journey time: 3½ hours

4325 (4-8) J. Staples & Co.

'THE ROCKET'

LONDON - WALTHAM CROSS - HODDESDON - WARE - HERTFORD
(24¼ miles).

LONDON Saracens Head, Snow Hill dep. 8 45 a.m.
HERTFORD   dep. 3 00 p.m.

Journey time: 3¾ hours

4388 (6-12) J. Carter

'THE REGULATOR'

LONDON - WALTHAM CROSS - HODDESDON - WARE - HERTFORD (23 miles).

LONDON Bell & Crown, Holborn dep. 3 00 p.m.
HERTFORD   dep. 8 00 a.m. Mon.
                                    9 00 a.m. Tu.-Sat.

Journey time : 4 hours

2911 (4-8) J. Hart

'THE GOOD INTENT'

LONDON - EALING - UXBRIDGE - HIGH WYCOMBE (31 miles).

LONDON New Inn, Old Bailey dep. 4 00 p.m.
HIGH WYCOMBE   dep. 9 00 a.m.

Journey time : 4 hours

3406 (6-12) J. Kershaw

'KERSHAW'S SAFETY COACH'

LONDON - BARNET - HATFIELD - HITCHIN (36 miles).

LONDON White Bear, Piccadilly   dep. 1 45 p.m.
Three Cups, Aldersgate Street dep. 2 30 p.m.
HITCHIN   dep. 6 00 a.m. Mon. & Fri.
                                      9 00 a.m. Tu.,Wed,Th.,Sat.

Journey time : 4½ hours

4374 (4-8) T. Guiver

''THE EMERALD'

LONDON - WALTHAM CROSS - HODDESDON (19 miles).

LONDON New Inn, Old Bailey dep. 2 30 p.m.
HODDESDON   dep. 8 00 a.m.

Journey time : 3 hours

4765 , 4771 (4-8) W. Chaplin & Co.

'THE REGULATOR'

LONDON - WOODFORD - EPPING - SAWBRIDGEWORTH - BISHOPS STORTFORD - GREAT CHESTERFORD - CAMBRIDGE - NEWMARKET - MILDENHALL - BRANDON - DEREHAM - HOLT (129 miles).

LONDON White Horse, Fetter Lane dep. 6 00 a.m.
HOLT   dep. 5 45 a.m.

Journey time : 15¾ hours

5326 (4-8) A. Kerr
'THE PERSEVERANCE'
LONDON - BARKING - AVELEY - HORNDON (23 miles).

LONDON The Bull, Aldgate dep. 4 00 p.m.
HORNDON dep. 7 30 a.m.
Journey time: 3½ hours

1463 (4-11) B.W. Horne & Co.
'THE STAR'
LONDON - MORDEN - EPSOM - LEATHERHEAD - DORKING - HORSHAM (37 miles).

LONDON Old Bell, Holborn dep. 3 00 p.m.
HORSHAM dep. 6 45 a.m.
Journey time: 4½ hours

3547 (4-8) B.W. Horne & Co.

LONDON - EDGWARE - ST. ALBANS - LUTON - BEDFORD - WELLINGBOROUGH - KETTERING (81 miles).

LONDON George & Blue Boar, Holborn dep. 8 00 a.m. Mon., Wed., Fri.
KETTERING dep. 7 00 a.m. Tu., Th., Sat.
Journey time: 10 hours

2912, 3134 (4-11) J. Hearn & Co.
'THE SOVEREIGN'

(A) LONDON - EALING - UXBRIDGE - AMERSHAM - WENDOVER - AYLESBURY - BICESTER - BANBURY - SOUTHAM - LEAMINGTON (96 miles).

(B) LONDON - EDGWARE - STANMORE - WATFORD - HEMEL HEMPSTEAD - BERKHAMSTED - TRING - AYLESBURY - BICESTER - BANBURY - SOUTHAM - LEAMINGTON (91 miles).

LONDON Kings Arms, Snow Hill dep. 8 00 a.m. Mon., Wed., Fri. (Route A)
8 45 a.m. Tu., Th., Sat. (Route B)
LEAMINGTON dep. 9 00 a.m. Mon., Wed., Fri. (Route B)
9 00 a.m. Tu., Th., Sat. (Route A)
Journey time:

3425, 3426, 3427 (4-11) E. Sherman & Co.
'THE EXPRESS'
LONDON - BARNET - ST. ALBANS - DUNSTABLE - WOBURN - NEWPORT PAGNELL - NORTHAMPTON - MARKET HARBOROUGH - LEICESTER - LOUGHBOROUGH - NOTTINGHAM - MANSFIELD - CHESTERFIELD - SHEFFIELD - BARNSLEY - WAKEFIELD - LEEDS (196 miles).

LONDON Bull & Mouth, St. Martin's-le-Grand dep. 4 30p.m.
LEEDS dep. 10 00a.m.
Journey time: 25½ hours

3443, 3445, 3552, 3553 (4-8) W. Smith & Co./B.W. Horne & Co.
'THE UNION'
LONDON - BARNET - HATFIELD - STEVENAGE - BALDOCK - BIGGLESWADE - EATON SOCON - NORMAN CROSS - STAMFORD - GRANTHAM - NEWARK - RETFORD - BAWTRY - DONCASTER - WAKEFIELD - LEEDS (191 miles).

LONDON Regent Circus, Piccadilly dep. 4 30p.m.
Golden Cross, Charing Cross dep. 5 45p.m.
LEEDS dep. 5 30p.m.
Journey time: 24 hours

3454, 3455, 3456, 3506 (4-11) J. Francis & Co.
'THE COURIER'
LONDON - BARNET - ST. ALBANS - DUNSTABLE - WOBURN - NEWPORT PAGNELL - NORTHAMPTON - MARKET HARBOROUGH - LEICESTER - LOUGHBOROUGH - NOTTINGHAM - MANSFIELD - CHESTERFIELD - SHEFFIELD - BARNSLEY - WAKEFIELD - LEEDS (197 miles).

LONDON Belle Sauvage, Ludgate Hill dep. 5 00p.m.
LEEDS dep. 6 00p.m.
Journey time: 24 hours

3469, 3470, 3479 (4-8) S.A. Mountain & Co.
'THE ROCKINGHAM'
LONDON - BARNET - HATFIELD - STEVENAGE - BALDOCK - BIGGLESWADE - EATON SOCON - NORMAN CROSS - STAMFORD - GRANTHAM - NEWARK - RETFORD - BAWTRY - DONCASTER - WAKEFIELD - LEEDS (190 miles).

LONDON Saracens Head, Snow Hill dep. 4 30p.m.
LEEDS dep. 9 00a.m.
Journey time: 23 hours

3490, 3519 (4-11) E. Sherman & Co.

'THE UNION'

LONDON - BARNET - ST. ALBANS - DUNSTABLE - WOBURN - NEWPORT PAGNELL - NORTHAMPTON - MARKET HARBOROUGH - LEICESTER (98 miles).

LONDON Bull & Mouth, St. Martin's-le-Grand dep. 6 30 a.m.
LEICESTER dep.

Journey time: 12 hours

1455 (4-8) B. W. Horne & Co.

LONDON - CROYDON - PURLEY - CATERHAM - GODSTONE - EAST GRINSTEAD - FOREST ROW - LEWES (50 miles).

LONDON Golden Cross, Charing Cross dep. 2 30 p.m. Tu, Th, Sat.
LEWES dep. Mon, Wed, Fri.

Journey time: 6½ hours

1453, 1454 (4-11) B. W. Horne & Co.

LONDON - CROYDON - PURLEY - CATERHAM - GODSTONE - EAST GRINSTEAD - FOREST ROW - LEWES (50 miles).

LONDON Golden Cross, Charing Cross dep. 9 30 a.m.
LEWES dep. 9 00 a.m.

Journey time: 6¼ hours

1449 (4-11) B. W. Horne & Co.

'THE COMET'

LONDON - MORDEN - EPSOM - LEATHERHEAD - DORKING - BILLINGSHURST - PULBOROUGH - ARUNDEL - LITTLEHAMPTON (59 miles).

LONDON Golden Cross, Charing Cross dep. 9 00 a.m. Mon, Wed, Fri.
LITTLEHAMPTON dep. 10 00 a.m. Tu, Th., Sat.

Journey time: 7½ hours

2091 (4-11) W. Chaplin & Co.

'THE ROYAL SUSSEX'

LONDON - KINGSTON - ESHER - GUILDFORD - GODALMING - MOUSEHILL - PETWORTH - ARUNDEL - LITTLEHAMPTON (64 miles).

LONDON Spread Eagle, Gracechurch Street dep. 7 15 a.m. Tu, Th, Sat.
LITTLEHAMPTON dep. 10 45 a.m. Mon, Wed, Fri.

Journey time: 8¼ hours

3438, 3441 (4-8), 3442, 3444 (4-11) W.Chaplin & Co.

'THE ALBION'

LONDON - BARNET - ST. ALBANS - DUNSTABLE - FENNY STRATFORD -
STONY STRATFORD - TOWCESTER - DAVENTRY - COVENTRY -
BIRMINGHAM - WOLVERHAMPTON - NEWPORT - WHITCHURCH - CHESTER -
WOODSIDE - LIVERPOOL (207 miles).

LONDON Swan with Two Necks, Lad Lane dep. 6 30p.m.
LIVERPOOL   dep.

Journey time: 24 hours

3477, 3494, 3539, 3541 (4-8) S.A. Mountain & Co.

'THE EXPRESS'

LONDON - BARNET - ST. ALBANS - DUNSTABLE - FENNY STRATFORD -
STONY STRATFORD - TOWCESTER - DAVENTRY - SOUTHAM -
LEAMINGTON - WARWICK - SOLIHULL - BIRMINGHAM - WALSALL -
CANNOCK - STAFFORD - STONE - NEWCASTLE - UNDER - LYME -
HOLMES CHAPEL - KNUTSFORD - WARRINGTON - LIVERPOOL
(218 miles).

LONDON Gloster Warehouse, Oxford Street dep. 5 00 p.m.
           Saracens Head, Snow Hill   dep. 5 30 p.m.
LIVERPOOL   dep. 5 30 p.m.

Journey time : 26 hours

3505, 3560, 3562, 3563 (4-11) B.W. Horne & Co.

'THE UMPIRE'

LONDON - BARNET - ST. ALBANS - DUNSTABLE - WOBURN - NEWPORT
PAGNELL - NORTHAMPTON - WELFORD - LUTTERWORTH - HINCKLEY -
ATHERSTONE - TAMWORTH - LICHFIELD - RUGELEY - STONE -
NEWCASTLE - UNDER - LYME - HOLMES CHAPEL - KNUTSFORD -
WARRINGTON - LIVERPOOL (211 miles).

LONDON Golden Cross, Charing Cross   dep. 2 00 p.m.
LIVERPOOL   dep. 12 00 noon

Journey time: 24 hours

3413 (4-8) A. Bryan

'THE TIMES'

LONDON - BARNET - ST. ALBANS - LUTON (31 miles).

LONDON Golden Lion, St. John Street dep. 5 00 p.m.
LUTON   dep. 8 00 a.m.

Journey time : 4 hours

3523 (6-3) T. Finch
Omnibus: 'THE INDUSTRY'
LONDON - BARNET - HATFIELD - WHEATHAMPSTEAD – LUTON
(33 miles).

    LONDON Saracens Head, Friday Street dep. 11 00 a.m. Tu., Th., Sat.
    LUTON   dep. 11 00 a.m. Mon., Wed., Fri.
               Journey time: 6 hours

4366 (4-8), 4410 (4-11) W. Chaplin & Co. / J. Binge & Co.
'THE UNION'
LONDON - WALTHAM CROSS - HODDESDON - WARE - PUCKERIDGE -
BUNTINGFORD - ROYSTON - CAMBRIDGE - ELY - DOWNHAM MARKET -
LYNN (98 miles).

    LONDON White Horse, Fetter Lane and
                Belle Sauvage, Ludgate Hill   dep. 8 00 a.m.
    LYNN   dep. 6 00 a.m.
              Journey time: 12 hours

407 (4-11) F. Scholfield & Co.
'THE BRITISH QUEEN'
LONDON - SIDCUP - FARNINGHAM - WROTHAM - MAIDSTONE (35 miles).
    LONDON Bull & Mouth, St. Martin's-le-Grand dep. 3 15 p.m.
    MAIDSTONE   dep. 6 00 a.m.
           Journey time: 4½ hours

408 (4-11) F. Scholfield & Co.
'THE FAVOURITE'
LONDON - SIDCUP - FARNINGHAM - WROTHAM - MAIDSTONE (35 miles).
    LONDON Bull & Mouth, St. Martin's-le-Grand dep. 9 00 a.m.
    MAIDSTONE   dep. 3 30 p.m.
           Journey time: 4½ hours

416 (7-5) J. Martin
'MARTIN'S OMNIBUS'
LONDON - SIDCUP - FARNINGHAM - WROTHAM - MAIDSTONE (35 miles).
    LONDON Saracens Head, Friday Street dep. 1 30 p.m., Tu., Th., Sat.
    MAIDSTONE   dep. 7 45 a.m. Mon., Wed., Fri.
           Journey time: 7 hours

497 (4-11) J. Egerton & Co.

'THE RELIANCE'

LONDON – SIDCUP – FARNINGHAM – WROTHAM – MEREWORTH – WATERINGBURY – MAIDSTONE (37 miles).

    LONDON Belle Sauvage, Ludgate Hill dep. 1 00 p.m.
    MAIDSTONE   dep. 8 00 a.m.
        Journey time : $4\frac{1}{2}$ hours

606 (4-11) W. Gilbert & Co.

'THE BALLOON'

LONDON – SIDCUP – FARNINGHAM – WROTHAM – MAIDSTONE (35 miles).

    LONDON Blossoms Inn, Lawrence Lane dep. 2 30 p.m.
    MAIDSTONE   dep. 9 00 a.m.
        Journey time : $4\frac{1}{2}$ hours

5002 (4-11) W. Woods & Co.

LONDON – ILFORD – ROMFORD – BRENTWOOD – CHELMSFORD – MALDON (42 miles).

    LONDON 220 Piccadilly   dep. 3 00 p.m.
    MALDON   dep. 6 00 a.m.
        Journey time : 6 hours

4954 (4-11) G. French

'THE TELEGRAPH'

LONDON – ILFORD – ROMFORD – BRENTWOOD – CHELMSFORD – MALDON (39 miles).

    LONDON The Bull, Aldgate   dep. 10 00 a.m. Wed., Fri., Sun.
    MALDON   dep. 11 00 a.m. Tu., Th., Sat.
        Journey time : 5 hours

3451, 3452 (4-11) E. Sherman & Co.

'THE TELEGRAPH'

LONDON – BARNET – ST. ALBANS – DUNSTABLE – WOBURN – NEWPORT PAGNELL – NORTHAMPTON – MARKET HARBOROUGH – LEICESTER – LOUGHBOROUGH – DERBY – ASHBOURNE – LEEK – MACCLESFIELD – STOCKPORT – MANCHESTER (191 miles).

    LONDON Bull & Mouth, St. Martin's-le-Grand   dep. 5 30 a.m.
    MANCHESTER   dep. 5 00 a.m.
        Journey time : $18\frac{1}{2}$ hours

3448, 3493 (4-8) E. Sherman & Co.
'THE RED ROVER'
LONDON - BARNET - ST. ALBANS - DUNSTABLE - FENNY STRATFORD -
STONY STRATFORD - TOWCESTER - DAVENTRY - COVENTRY -
BIRMINGHAM - LICHFIELD - RUGELEY - STAFFORD - STONE -
NEWCASTLE - UNDER - LYME - CONGLETON - WILMSLOW - MANCHESTER
(187 miles).

LONDON Bull & Mouth, St. Martin's-le-Grand dep. 8 30 a.m.
MANCHESTER   dep. 8 00 a.m.
Journey time: 20 hours

3467, 3468, 3529 (4-8) W. Chaplin & Co.
'THE ROYAL DEFIANCE'
LONDON - BARNET - ST. ALBANS - DUNSTABLE - WOBURN - NEWPORT
PAGNELL - NORTHAMPTON - MARKET HARBOROUGH - LEICESTER -
LOUGHBOROUGH - DERBY - ASHBOURNE - LEEK - MACCLESFIELD -
STOCKPORT - MANCHESTER (187 miles).

LONDON Swan with Two Necks, Lad Lane   dep. 5 30 p.m.
MANCHESTER   dep. 6 00 p.m.
Journey time: 20 hours

3472, 3474, 3484 (4-8) W. Chaplin & Co.
'THE ROYAL BRUCE'
LONDON - BARNET - ST. ALBANS - DUNSTABLE - WOBURN - NEWPORT
PAGNELL - NORTHAMPTON - MARKET HARBOROUGH - LEICESTER -
LOUGHBOROUGH - DERBY - ASHBOURNE - LEEK - MACCLESFIELD -
STOCKPORT - MANCHESTER (186 miles).

LONDON Swan with Two Necks, Lad Lane   dep. 7 00 p.m.
MANCHESTER   dep. 12 00 noon
Journey time: 22½ hours

3480, 3481, 3558, 3559 (4-11) W. Gilbert & Co. / B. W. Horne & Co.
'PEVERIL OF THE PEAK'
LONDON - EDGWARE - ST. ALBANS - LUTON - BEDFORD - RUSHDEN -
KETTERING - MARKET HARBOROUGH - LEICESTER - LOUGHBOROUGH -
DERBY - MATLOCK - BAKEWELL - BUXTON - STOCKPORT - MANCHESTER
(189 miles).

LONDON Golden Cross, Charing Cross and
        Blossoms Inn, Lawrence Lane   dep. 7 45 p.m.
MANCHESTER   dep. 12 00 noon
Journey time: 21 hours

3496, 3497, 3498 (4-11) J. Clare & Co.

'THE BEEHIVE'

LONDON - BARNET - ST. ALBANS - DUNSTABLE - FENNY STRATFORD - STONY STRATFORD - TOWCESTER - DAVENTRY - COVENTRY - BIRMINGHAM - WOLVERHAMPTON - STAFFORD - STONE - NEWCASTLE-UNDER-LYME - CONGLETON - MACCLESFIELD - STOCKPORT - MANCHESTER (196 miles).

LONDON Belle Sauvage, Ludgate Hill dep. 8 00 a.m.
MANCHESTER   dep.
Journey time: 20½ hours

2250 (4-11) F. Wyatt & Co.

'THE ORIGINAL MARLOW COACH'

LONDON - HOUNSLOW - SLOUGH - MAIDENHEAD - MARLOW (34 miles).
LONDON Blossoms Inn, Lawrence Lane dep. 2 00 p.m.
MARLOW   dep. 7 00 a.m.
Journey time: 4½ hours

1805, 1830 (4-8) E. Stammers / W. Smith & Co.

'THE DILIGENT'

LONDON - KINGSTON - ESHER - GUILDFORD - GODALMING - MOUSEHILL (37 miles).
LONDON The Angel, St. Clements dep. 10 30 a.m.
MOUSEHILL   dep.
Journey time: 5 hours

2102, 2103 (4-11) W. Batten & Co.

'THE ORIGINAL NEWBURY COACH'

LONDON - HOUNSLOW - SLOUGH - MAIDENHEAD - READING - NEWBURY (58 miles).
LONDON Belle Sauvage, Ludgate Hill dep. 11 15 a.m.
NEWBURY   dep. 9 00 a.m.
Journey time: 6¾ hours

4354, 4355, 4356, 4357 (4-11) E. Sherman & Co.

'THE LORD WELLINGTON'

LONDON - WALTHAM CROSS - HODDESDON - WARE - PUCKERIDGE - BUNTINGFORD - ROYSTON - HUNTINGDON - NORMAN CROSS - STAMFORD - GRANTHAM - NEWARK - RETFORD - BAWTRY - DONCASTER - FERRYBRIDGE - TADCASTER - YORK - EASINGWOLD - THIRSK - NORTHALLERTON - DARLINGTON - DURHAM - NEWCASTLE UPON TYNE (278 miles).

LONDON Bull & Mouth, St. Martin's-le-Grand dep. 3 30 p.m.
NEWCASTLE UPON TYNE   dep. 10 00 a.m.
Journey time: 31 hours

3434, 3440 (4-11) E. Sherman & Co.
'THE NORTHAMPTON'
LONDON - BARNET - ST. ALBANS - DUNSTABLE - WOBURN - NEWPORT PAGNELL - NORTHAMPTON (66 miles).

LONDON Bull & Mouth, St. Martin's-le-Grand dep. 12 00 noon
NORTHAMPTON, Angel Hotel dep. 9 30 a.m.
Journey time: 7 hours

4730, 4731 (4-8) W. Chaplin & Co.
'THE MAGNET'
LONDON - WOODFORD - EPPING - SAWBRIDGEWORTH - BISHOPS STORTFORD - GREAT CHESTERFORD - NEWMARKET - THETFORD - ATTLEBOROUGH - WYMONDHAM - NORWICH (110 miles).

LONDON White Horse, Fetter Lane dep. 7 00 p.m.
NORWICH dep. 6 00 p.m.
Journey time: 11 hours

4975 (4-11) W. Chaplin & Co.
'THE TIMES'
LONDON - ILFORD - ROMFORD - BRENTWOOD - CHELMSFORD - BRAINTREE - HALSTEAD - SUDBURY - LONG MELFORD - BURY ST. EDMUNDS - DISS - NORWICH (112 miles).

LONDON Spread Eagle, Gracechurch Street dep. 6 30 a.m. Tu., Th., Sat.
NORWICH dep. 6 30 a.m. Mon., Wed., Fri.
Journey time: 13 hours

4944, 5011 (4-11) J. Nelson & Co.
'THE PHENOMENA'
LONDON - ILFORD - ROMFORD - BRENTWOOD - CHELMSFORD - BRAINTREE - HALSTEAD - SUDBURY - LONG MELFORD - BURY ST. EDMUNDS - DISS - NORWICH (117 miles).

LONDON 52 Piccadilly and
Belle Sauvage, Ludgate Hill dep. 6 00 a.m.
NORWICH dep. 6 30 a.m.
Journey time: $13\frac{1}{2}$ hours

4754, 4755 (4-11) B. W. Horne & Co.
'THE TELEGRAPH'
LONDON - WOODFORD - EPPING - SAWBRIDGEWORTH - BISHOPS STORTFORD - GREAT CHESTERFORD - NEWMARKET - THETFORD - ATTLEBOROUGH - WYMONDHAM - NORWICH (112 miles).

LONDON Golden Cross, Charing Cross dep. 7 00 a.m.
NORWICH dep. 7 00 a.m.
Journey time: 12 hours

3464, 3465 (4-8) W. Chaplin & Co.

'THE TIMES'

LONDON - BARNET - ST. ALBANS - DUNSTABLE - WOBURN - NEWPORT PAGNELL - NORTHAMPTON - MARKET HARBOROUGH - LEICESTER - LOUGHBOROUGH - NOTTINGHAM (124 miles).

LONDON Swan with Two Necks, Lad Lane dep. 6 45 a.m.
NOTTINGHAM   dep. 6 00 a.m.

Journey time: 14¾ hours

3568, 3569 (4-8) W. Chaplin & Co.

'THE COMMERCIAL'

LONDON - BARNET - ST. ALBANS - DUNSTABLE - WOBURN - NEWPORT PAGNELL - NORTHAMPTON - MARKET HARBOROUGH - LEICESTER - LOUGHBOROUGH - NOTTINGHAM (124 miles).

LONDON Swan with Two Necks, Lad Lane dep. 4 45 p.m.
NOTTINGHAM   dep.

Journey time: 18¼ hours

4950 (4-11) E. Deacon & Co.

LONDON - ILFORD - ROMFORD - HORNCHURCH - OCKENDON (20 miles).

LONDON Saracens Head, Aldgate   dep. 4 00 p.m.
OCKENDON   dep. 7 30 a.m.

Journey time: 3¼ hours

4942 (4-11) J. West

LONDON - CHIGWELL - ABRIDGE - ONGAR (21 miles).

LONDON The Bull, Aldgate   dep. 2 45 p.m.
ONGAR   dep. 8 00 a.m.

Journey time: 3 hours

---

414 (4-8) R. Gates

LONDON - BROMLEY - ORPINGTON (16 miles).

	MON.WED.SAT.	TU.TH.FRI.
LONDON The Ship, Charing Cross dep.	—	3 30 p.m.
The George, Borough dep.	4 00 p.m.	4 00 p.m.
ORPINGTON dep.	7 30 a.m.	7 30 a.m.

Journey time: 2½ / 3 hours

3544 (4-11) B.W. Horne & Co.
'THE REGULATOR'
LONDON - BARNET - HATFIELD - STEVENAGE - BALDOCK - BIGGLESWADE -
ST. NEOTS - KIMBOLTON - THRAPSTON - OUNDLE (85 miles).

    LONDON George & Blue Boar, Holborn dep. 7 00 a.m. Tu., Th., Sat.
    OUNDLE   dep. 7 00 a.m. Mon., Wed., Fri.
          Journey time: 10 hours

2100, 2101 (4-11) R. Nelson & Co.
'THE DEFIANCE'
LONDON - HOUNSLOW - SLOUGH - MAIDENHEAD - HENLEY - OXFORD (60 miles).

    LONDON Belle Sauvage, Ludgate Hill dep. 1 30 p.m.
    OXFORD   dep.
          Journey time: 6½ hours

2229, 2239 (4-11) B.W. Horne & Co.
'THE ALERT'
LONDON - HOUNSLOW - SLOUGH - MAIDENHEAD - HENLEY - OXFORD (61 miles).

    LONDON Cross Keys, Wood Street dep. 9 00 a.m.
    OXFORD
          Journey time: 7 hours

2919, 2920 (4-11) E. Sherman & Co.
'THE BLENHEIM'
LONDON - EALING - UXBRIDGE - HIGH WYCOMBE - OXFORD (57 miles).

    LONDON Bull & Mouth, St. Martin's-le-Grand dep. 10 00 a.m.
    OXFORD   dep. 10 00 a.m.
          Journey time: 6 hours

2968, 2969 (4-11) G. Tollitt
'THE AGE'
LONDON - EALING - UXBRIDGE - HIGH WYCOMBE - OXFORD (57 miles).

    LONDON Swan with Two Necks, Lad Lane   dep. 1 00 p.m.
    OXFORD   dep. 10 30 a.m.
          Journey time: 6 hours

3106 (4-8), 3135 (4-5) G. Stanborough

LONDON - HARROW - PINNER (15 miles).

    LONDON The Bull, Holborn   dep. 9 00 a.m., 3 00 p.m.
    PINNER   dep. 9 00 a.m., 3 00 p.m.
          Journey time: 2 hours

1816, 1817 (6-9) J. Alexander & Co.

A Coach Van

LONDON - KINGSTON - ESHER - GUILDFORD - GODALMING - MOUSEHILL - PETERSFIELD - HORNDEAN - PORTSMOUTH (73 miles).

LONDON Castle & Falcon, Aldersgate dep. 4 00 p.m.
PORTSMOUTH dep. 4 00 p.m.

Journey time : 17 hours

1813 (4-8) T. Moore & Co.

'THE ROYAL BLUE'

LONDON - KINGSTON - ESHER - GUILDFORD - GODALMING - MOUSEHILL - PETERSFIELD - HORNDEAN - PORTSMOUTH (73 miles).

LONDON New Inn, Old Change dep. 7 00 a.m. Tu., Th., Sat.
PORTSMOUTH dep. 6 00 a.m. Mon., Wed., Fri.

Journey time : 11 hours

1827, 1829 (4-11) B.W. Horne & Co. / W. Chaplin & Co.

'THE INDEPENDENT'

LONDON - KINGSTON - ESHER - GUILDFORD - GODALMING - MOUSEHILL - PETERSFIELD - HORNDEAN - PORTSMOUTH (73 miles).

LONDON Golden Cross, Charing Cross and
Spread Eagle, Gracechurch Street dep. 9 00 a.m.
PORTSMOUTH dep.

Journey time : 10 hours

1944, 2053 (4-11) W. Chaplin & Co.

'THE STAR OF BRUNSWICK'

LONDON - KINGSTON - ESHER - GUILDFORD - GODALMING - MOUSEHILL - PETERSFIELD - HORNDEAN - PORTSMOUTH (73 miles).

LONDON Spread Eagle, Gracechurch Street dep. 8 00 a.m.
PORTSMOUTH dep.

Journey time : 9 hours

2056, 2236 (4-11) R. Gray & Co. / E. Sherman & Co.

'THE REGULATOR'

LONDON - KINGSTON - ESHER - GUILDFORD - GODALMING - MOUSEHILL - PETERSFIELD - HORNDEAN - PORTSMOUTH (72 miles).

LONDON Bolt-in-Tun, Fleet Street and
Bull & Mouth, St. Martin's-le-Grand dep. 8 30 a.m.
PORTSMOUTH dep.

Journey time : 9 hours

1985, 2247 (4-11) J. Hearn & Co.
                    'THE TIMES'
LONDON - KINGSTON - ESHER - GUILDFORD - GODALMING - MOUSEHILL -
PETERSFIELD - HORNDEAN - PORTSMOUTH (72 miles).
            LONDON Kings Arms, Snow Hill dep. 12.00 noon
            PORTSMOUTH   dep.
                Journey time :

2095, 2096 (4-11) G. Vicat & Co.
                    'THE ROCKET'
LONDON - KINGSTON - ESHER - GUILDFORD - GODALMING - MOUSEHILL -
PETERSFIELD - HORNDEAN - PORTSMOUTH (72 miles).
            LONDON Belle Sauvage, Ludgate Hill dep. 7 45 a.m.
            PORTSMOUTH   dep. 9 00 a.m.
                Journey time : 8¼ hours

2097, 2098 (4-8) G. Vicat & Co.
                    'THE ROCKET'
LONDON - KINGSTON - ESHER - GUILDFORD - GODALMING - MOUSEHILL -
PETERSFIELD - HORNDEAN - PORTSMOUTH (72 miles).
            LONDON Belle Sauvage, Ludgate Hill dep. 8 30 p.m.
            PORTSMOUTH   dep.
                Journey time : 9 hours

3439 (4-5) J. Horsley & Co,

LONDON - BARNET - POTTERS BAR (15½ miles).
            LONDON Boar & Castle, Oxford Street   dep. 3 00 p.m.
            POTTERS BAR   dep.
                Journey time : 2¼ hours

2015 (4-11) S. Williams & Co,
                'THE NEW POST COACH'
LONDON - HOUNSLOW - STAINES - EGHAM - ASCOT - BRACKNELL -
WOKINGHAM - READING (41 miles).
            LONDON Black Lion, Water Lane   dep. 3 00 p.m.
            READING   dep.
                Journey time : 5 hours

2020,2021 (4-11) S. Williams & Co.
'THE FOREST COACH'
LONDON - HOUNSLOW - STAINES - WINDSOR PARK - WINKFIELD -
BINFIELD - WOKINGHAM - READING (41 miles).
LONDON Black Lion, Water Lane   dep. 3 00p.m.
READING   dep.
Journey time: 5½ hours

2117, 2139 (4-11) R. Gray & Co.
'MATCHAM'S COACH'
LONDON - HOUNSLOW - SLOUGH - MAIDENHEAD - READING
(41 miles).
LONDON Cross Keys, Wood Street dep. 12 00 noon
READING   dep. 12 00 noon
Journey time: 4½ hours

2217 (7-5) R. Seymour
An Accommodation Coach
LONDON - HOUNSLOW - STAINES - EGHAM - ASCOT - BRACKNELL -
WOKINGHAM - READING (42 miles).
LONDON Saracens Head, Friday Street dep. 10 00a.m. Tu., Th., Sat.
READING   dep. 8 00a.m. Mon., Wed., Fri.
Journey time: 6 hours

2220,2221 (4-11) W. Gilbert & Co.
'THE TELEGRAPH'
LONDON - HOUNSLOW - SLOUGH - MAIDENHEAD - READING
(41 miles).
LONDON Blossoms Inn, Lawrence Lane dep. 11 00 a.m.
READING   dep.
Journey time 4¼ hours

1277 (4-11) H. Crunden

LONDON - SUTTON - REIGATE (22 miles).
LONDON Cross Keys, Gracechurch Street dep. 3 30p.m.
REIGATE   dep. 8 00a.m.
Journey time: 3 hours

3126 (4-8) W. Wyatt & Co.

LONDON - HARROW - PINNER - NORTHWOOD - RICKMANSWORTH
(20 miles).
      LONDON The Bull, Holborn   dep. 4 00 p.m.
      RICKMANSWORTH   dep.
         Journey time: 3 hours

479, 480 (4-11) R. Gray & Co.
         'THE SOVEREIGN'
LONDON - BROMLEY - FARNBOROUGH - SEVENOAKS - TONBRIDGE -
LAMBERHURST - HAWKHURST - RYE (64 miles).
      LONDON Bolt-in-Tun, Fleet Street dep. 11 00 a.m.
      RYE   dep. 8 00 a.m.
         Journey time: 9 hours

3102, 3103 (4-8) A. Bryan

LONDON - EDGWARE - ST. ALBANS (21 miles).
      LONDON The Ram, Smithfield   dep. 2 00 p.m.
      ST. ALBANS   dep. 9 00 a.m.
         Journey time: 3 hours

2083, 2084 (4-11) W. Chaplin & Co.
         'THE LIGHT SALISBURY'
LONDON - HOUNSLOW - STAINES - EGHAM - BAGSHOT - CAMBERLEY -
HARTLEY WINTNEY - BASINGSTOKE - STOCKBRIDGE - SALISBURY
(83 miles).
      LONDON White Horse, Fetter Lane dep. 7 45 a.m.
      SALISBURY White Hart   dep. 8 00 a.m.
         Journey time: 10 hours

2123, 2124 (6-9) R. Fagg & Co.
         'THE OLD SALISBURY COACH'
LONDON - HOUNSLOW - STAINES - EGHAM - BAGSHOT - CAMBERLEY -
HARTLEY WINTNEY - BASINGSTOKE - STOCKBRIDGE - SALISBURY
(83 miles).
      LONDON White Bear, Basinghall Street dep. 6 30 p.m.
      SALISBURY Black Horse   dep. 5 30 p.m.
         Journey time: 14 hours

456 (4-11) J. Stephens & Co.
'THE UNITED FRIENDS'
LONDON - BROMLEY - SEVENOAKS (24½ miles).

LONDON Bolt-in-Tun, Fleet Street   dep. 3 30 p.m.
SEVENOAKS   dep. 8 00 a.m.
Journey time: 3½ hours

3127 (4-5) J. Billing

LONDON - EDGWARE - SHENLEY HILL (17 miles).

LONDON Blue Posts, Holborn   dep. 4 00 p.m.
SHENLEY   dep. 8 00 a.m.
Journey time : 3 hours

2916, 2917, 2918 (4-11) E. Sherman & Co.
'THE SALOPIAN'
LONDON - HOUNSLOW - SLOUGH - MAIDENHEAD - HENLEY - OXFORD - WOODSTOCK - SHIPSTON-ON-STOUR — STRATFORD-UPON-AVON - BIRMINGHAM - WOLVERHAMPTON - SHIFNAL - IRONBRIDGE - SHREWSBURY (163 miles).

LONDON Bull & Mouth, St. Martin's-le-Grand dep. 6 30 a.m.
SHREWSBURY Talbot Hotel   dep. 7 00 a.m.
Journey time : 18 hours

3428, 3429 (4-11) E. Sherman & Co.
'THE WONDER'
LONDON - BARNET - ST. ALBANS - DUNSTABLE - FENNY STRATFORD - STONY STRATFORD - TOWCESTER - DAVENTRY - COVENTRY - BIRMINGHAM - WOLVERHAMPTON - SHIFNAL - WELLINGTON - SHREWSBURY (153 miles).

LONDON Bull & Mouth, St. Martin's-le-Grand dep. 7 00 a.m.
SHREWSBURY The Lion   dep. 5 45 a.m.
Journey time : 15¾ hours

3475, 3476 (4-8) E. Sherman & Co.
'THE STAG'
LONDON - BARNET - ST. ALBANS - DUNSTABLE - FENNY STRATFORD - STONY STRATFORD - TOWCESTER - DAVENTRY - COVENTRY - BIRMINGHAM - WOLVERHAMPTON - SHIFNAL - WELLINGTON - SHREWSBURY (153 miles).

LONDON Bull & Mouth, St. Martin's-le-Grand dep. 6 00 a.m.
SHREWSBURY The Lion   dep. 4 45 a.m.
Journey time : 16 hours

3246, 3247 (4-8) B.W. Horne & Co.
'THE NIMROD'
LONDON - BARNET- ST. ALBANS - DUNSTABLE - FENNY STRATFORD -
STONY STRATFORD - TOWCESTER - DAVENTRY - SOUTHAM -
LEAMINGTON - WARWICK - SOLIHULL - BIRMINGHAM - WOLVERHAMPTON -
SHIFNAL - WELLINGTON - SHREWSBURY (155 miles).

LONDON Old Bell, Holborn   dep. 6 30 a.m.
SHREWSBURY, Talbot Hotel   dep. 5 30 a.m.
Journey time: 16 hours

1902, 1903 (4-11) A. Collyer & Co.
'THE TIMES'
LONDON - KINGSTON - ESHER - GUILDFORD - FARNHAM - ALTON -
ALRESFORD - WINCHESTER - SOUTHAMPTON (79 miles).

LONDON Belle Sauvage, Ludgate Hill dep. 7 00 a.m.
SOUTHAMPTON   dep.
Journey time: 10 hours

1999, 2106 (4-11) J. Nelson & Co./ W. Chaplin & Co.
'THE INDEPENDENT'
LONDON - HOUNSLOW - STAINES - EGHAM - BAGSHOT - CAMBERLEY -
HARTLEY WINTNEY - BASINGSTOKE - WINCHESTER - SOUTHAMPTON
(77 miles).

LONDON The Bull, Aldgate and
         Spread Eagle, Gracechurch Street dep. 7 00 a.m.
SOUTHAMPTON   dep. 7 00 a.m.
Journey time: 10 hours

2121, 2122 (5-10) W. Chaplin & Co/ R. Fagg & Co.
'THE ROYAL WILLIAM'
LONDON - KINGSTON - ESHER - GUILDFORD - FARNHAM - ALTON -
ALRESFORD - WINCHESTER - SOUTHAMPTON (78 miles).

LONDON Swan with Two Necks, Lad Lane and
         White Bear, Basinghall Street dep. 6 30 p.m.
SOUTHAMPTON   dep. 7 30 p.m.
Journey time: 12 hours

2058, 2254 (4-11) R. Gray & Co.
'THE RED ROVER'
LONDON - KINGSTON - ESHER - GUILDFORD - FARNHAM - ALTON -
ALRESFORD - WINCHESTER - SOUTHAMPTON (78 miles).

LONDON Bolt-in-Tun, Fleet Street dep. 8 30 a.m.
SOUTHAMPTON dep. 9 45 a.m.
Journey time : 8 hours

2266, 2267 (4-8) R. Fagg & Co./W. Chaplin & Co.
'THE QUICKSILVER'
LONDON - HOUNSLOW - STAINES - EGHAM - BAGSHOT - CAMBERLEY -
HARTLEY WINTNEY - BASINGSTOKE - WINCHESTER - SOUTHAMPTON
(78 miles).

LONDON White Bear, Basinghall Street dep. 11 00 a.m.
SOUTHAMPTON dep. 11 45 a.m.
Journey time : 8 hours

2114 (4-11), 2133 (4-8) S. A. Mountain & Co./R. Fagg & Co.
'THE ECLIPSE'
LONDON - HOUNSLOW - STAINES - EGHAM - BAGSHOT - CAMBERLEY -
HARTLEY WINTNEY - BASINGSTOKE - WINCHESTER - SOUTHAMPTON
(77 miles).

LONDON Saracens Head, Snow Hill and
White Bear, Basinghall Street dep. 10 00 a.m.
SOUTHAMPTON dep. 10 45 a.m.
Journey time : 8 hours

2197, 2208 (4-8) J. Hearn & Co./R. Gray & Co.
'ALPHA'
LONDON - HOUNSLOW - STAINES - EGHAM - BAGSHOT - CAMBERLEY -
HARTLEY WINTNEY - BASINGSTOKE - WINCHESTER - SOUTHAMPTON
(79 miles).

LONDON Kings Arms, Snow Hill dep. 9 00 a.m.
SOUTHAMPTON dep.
Journey time :

2223, 2224 (4-11) B. W. Horne & Co.
'THE TELEGRAPH'
LONDON - HOUNSLOW - STAINES - EGHAM - BAGSHOT - CAMBERLEY -
HARTLEY WINTNEY - BASINGSTOKE - WINCHESTER - SOUTHAMPTON
(77 miles).

LONDON Cross Keys, Wood Street dep. 7 15 a.m.
SOUTHAMPTON dep. 7 45 a.m.
Journey time : 8 hours

536 (4 —) W. Harris

LONDON - BROMLEY - FARNBOROUGH - SEVENOAKS - TONBRIDGE -
SOUTHBOROUGH (32½ miles).

　　　　LONDON Catherine Wheel, Borough dep.　　p.m. Tu., Fri.
　　　　SOUTHBOROUGH　　　　　　　　dep.　　　　Mon., Thur.
　　　　　Journey time :

5000 (4 - 11) J. Tabor & Co.
　　　　　　　　'THE DESPATCH'
LONDON - ILFORD - ROMFORD - BRENTWOOD - BILLERICAY - WICKFORD -
RAYLEIGH - ROCHFORD - SOUTHEND-ON-SEA (44 miles).

　　　　LONDON The Bull, Aldgate　　dep. 2.45 p.m.
　　　　SOUTHEND-ON-SEA　　　　dep. 7.45 a.m.
　　　　　Journey time : 6 hours

3550 (4 - 11) B. W. Horne & Co.
　　　　　'THE REGENT'
LONDON - BARNET - HATFIELD - STEVENAGE - BALDOCK - BIGGLESWADE -
EATON SOCON - ST. NEOTS - HUNTINGDON - NORMAN CROSS - STAMFORD
(87 miles).

　　　　LONDON George & Blue Boar, Holborn dep. 8.00 a.m. Mon., Wed., Fri.
　　　　STAMFORD　　　　　　　　dep. 7.00 a.m. Tu., Th., Sat.
　　　　　Journey time : 12 hours

4390 (4 - 11) R. Fagg & Co.
　　　　　'THE DEFIANCE'
LONDON - WALTHAM CROSS - HODDESDON - WARE - PUCKERIDGE -
BUNTINGFORD - ROYSTON - HUNTINGDON - NORMAN CROSS - STAMFORD
(87 miles).

　　　　LONDON Bell & Crown, Holborn　　dep. 8.00 a.m. Tu., Th., Sat.
　　　　STAMFORD　　　　　　　　dep. 7.00 a.m. Mon., Wed., Fri.
　　　　　Journey time : 11¾ hours

2232 (4 - 11) B. W. Horne & Co.

LONDON - HOUNSLOW - SLOUGH - MAIDENHEAD - HENLEY - ABINGDON -
FARINGDON - LECHLADE - FAIRFORD - CIRENCESTER - STROUD
(103 miles).

　　　　LONDON Old Bell, Holborn　　dep. 7.30 a.m. Tu., Th., Sat.
　　　　STROUD　　　　　　　dep.　　　　Mon., Wed., Fri.
　　　　　Journey time :

4955 (4-11) W. Boston & Co.
'THE SUDBURY COACH'
LONDON - ILFORD - ROMFORD - BRENTWOOD - CHELMSFORD - BRAINTREE -
HALSTEAD - SUDBURY (56 miles).

LONDON Belle Sauvage, Ludgate Hill dep. 12 00 noon Tu., Th., Sat.
SUDBURY   dep. 10 00 a.m. Mon., Wed., Fri.
Journey time: 7 hours

---

428 (4-11) J. Nicholson & Co.
'THE TIMES'
LONDON - BROMLEY - WESTERHAM - BRASTED - SUNDRIDGE (26 miles)

LONDON Boar & Castle, Oxford Street dep. 3 00 p.m.
SUNDRIDGE   dep. 7 00 a.m.
Journey time: 4 hours

2043, 2044, 2045 (4-11) E. Sherman & Co.
'THE NORTH DEVON TELEGRAPH'
★ LONDON - HOUNSLOW - STAINES - EGHAM - BAGSHOT - CAMBERLEY -
HARTLEY WINTNEY - BASINGSTOKE - WHITCHURCH - ANDOVER - SALISBURY -
WILTON - HINDON - MERE - WINCANTON - LANGPORT - TAUNTON (147 miles).

LONDON Bull & Mouth, St. Martin's-le-Grand dep. 3 45 p.m.
TAUNTON   dep.
Journey time: 20 hours

★ Section of route London — Barnstaple. The service between Taunton
and Barnstaple provided by proprietor at Taunton.

424, 521 (4-8) W. Pawley & Co.
'THE TALLY - HO'
LONDON - SIDCUP - FARNINGHAM - WROTHAM - MEREWORTH -
WATERINGBURY - MAIDSTONE - HEADCORN - BIDDENDEN -
TENTERDEN (58 miles).

LONDON British Coffee House, Cockspur Street dep. 1 00 p.m.
TENTERDEN   dep. 6 45 a.m.
Journey time: 7¼ hours

2901 (4-8), 2905 (4-11) W. Taplin
'THE THAME SAFETY COACH'
LONDON - EALING - UXBRIDGE - HIGH WYCOMBE - PRINCES RISBOROUGH -
THAME (46 miles).

LONDON The Bull, Holborn dep. 9 00 a.m.
THAME   dep.
Journey time: 6 hours

2927 (5–1) J. Coles

An Omnibus

LONDON – EALING – UXBRIDGE – HIGH WYCOMBE – STOKENCHURCH – THAME (46 miles).

LONDON The Greyhound, Holborn dep. 9 00 a.m. Tu., Th., Sat.

THAME dep. 9 00 a.m. Mon., Wed., Fri.

Journey time:

3113 (4-8) J. Hearn & Co.

LONDON – EDGWARE – STANMORE – WATFORD – HEMEL HEMPSTEAD – BERKHAMSTED – TRING (33½ miles).

LONDON Kings Arms, Snow Hill dep. 3 00 p.m.

TRING dep. 8 00 a.m

Journey time: 5 hours

---

419 (4-8) T. Skinner & Co.

'THE AGE'

LONDON – BROMLEY – FARNBOROUGH – SEVENOAKS – TONBRIDGE – TUNBRIDGE WELLS (40 miles).

LONDON British Coffee House, Cockspur Street dep. 8 30 a.m.

TUNBRIDGE WELLS dep. 4 00 p.m.

Journey time: 5 hours

---

481 (4-11) R. Gray & Co.

'THE MORNING STAR'

LONDON – BROMLEY – FARNBOROUGH – SEVENOAKS – TONBRIDGE – TUNBRIDGE WELLS (37 miles).

LONDON Bolt-in-Tun, Fleet Street dep. 2 30 p.m.

TUNBRIDGE WELLS dep. 8 00 a.m.

Journey time: 4½ hours

---

501 (4-8) E. Churchill

'THE INDEPENDENT'

LONDON – BROMLEY – FARNBOROUGH – SEVENOAKS – TONBRIDGE – TUNBRIDGE WELLS (36½ miles).

LONDON Belle Sauvage, Ludgate Hill dep. 3 00 p.m.

TUNBRIDGE WELLS dep. 9 00 a.m.

Journey time: 4½ hours

518 (4-11) B.W. Horne & Co.
'THE SUSSEX'
LONDON - BROMLEY - FARNBOROUGH - SEVENOAKS - TONBRIDGE -
TUNBRIDGE WELLS (37 miles).

      LONDON Golden Cross, Charing Cross dep. 9 15 a.m,
      TUNBRIDGE WELLS   dep. 3 30p.m.
          Journey time: $4\frac{1}{2}$ hours

---

550 (4-11) B.W. Horne & Co.
'THE TELEGRAPH'
LONDON - BROMLEY - FARNBOROUGH - SEVENOAKS - TONBRIDGE -
TUNBRIDGE WELLS (37 miles).

      LONDON Golden Cross, Charing Cross dep. 3 45 p.m.
      TUNBRIDGE WELLS   dep. 10 00 a.m,
          Journey time: $4\frac{1}{2}$ hours

---

546 (4-11) B.W. Horne & Co.
'THE UNION'
LONDON - BROMLEY - FARNBOROUGH - SEVENOAKS - TONBRIDGE -
TUNBRIDGE WELLS (38 miles).

      LONDON George & Blue Boar, Holborn dep.
      TUNBRIDGE WELLS   dep. 11 00 a.m.
          Journey time :

2939 (4-11) R. Nash

LONDON - EALING - UXBRIDGE (17 miles).
      LONDON Clemmitts Inn, Old Bailey dep. 6 00 p.m,
      UXBRIDGE   dep.
          Journey time: $2\frac{1}{4}$ hours

2925 (6-12), 2907, 2926, 2927, 2937 (4-11) W. Tollitt
TOLLITT'S COACHES
LONDON - EALING - UXBRIDGE (17 miles).

  LONDON The Bull, Holborn dep. 10 00 a.m., 12 00 noon, 4 00, 5 00, 5 45 p.m
  UXBRIDGE   dep.
          Journey time: $2\frac{1}{4}$ hours

2938 (4-11) R. Green

LONDON - EALING - UXBRIDGE (17 miles).
      LONDON New Inn, Old Bailey dep. 4 00 p.m.
      UXBRIDGE   dep.
          Journey time :

3546 (4-11) B.W. Horne & Co.

LONDON - BARNET - HATFIELD - HITCHIN - SHEFFORD - BEDFORD -
RUSHDEN - KETTERING - ROCKINGHAM - UPPINGHAM (89 miles).
    LONDON George & Blue Boar, Holborn dep. 8 00 a.m. Tu., Th., Sat.
    UPPINGHAM   dep. 8 00 a.m. Mon., Wed., Fri.
               Journey time : 11 hours

2018, 2019 (4-8) T. Stevens & Co.

LONDON - HOUNSLOW - SLOUGH - MAIDENHEAD - HENLEY -
WALLINGFORD (48 miles).
      LONDON New Inn, Old Bailey   dep. 2 00 p.m.
      WALLINGFORD   dep.
            Journey time :

4391 (4-11) R. Fagg & Co.

LONDON - WALTHAM CROSS - HODDESDON - WARE (23 miles).
      LONDON Bell & Crown, Holborn dep. 4 00 p.m.
      WARE   dep. 6 00 a.m. Mon.
                      8 00 a.m. Tu. - Sat.
          Journey time: 3 hours

2936, 2940 (4-11) R. Nelson & Co. / W. Chaplin & Co.
               'THE HOPE'
LONDON - EALING - UXBRIDGE - HIGH WYCOMBE - OXFORD -
DEDDINGTON - BANBURY - SOUTHAM - LEAMINGTON - WARWICK
(100 miles).
      LONDON Belle Sauvage, Ludgate Hill and
           Swan with Two Necks, Lad Lane dep. 8 30 a.m.
      WARWICK
          Journey time: 11½ hours

3123 (4-8) W. Gilbert & Co.

LONDON - EDGWARE - STANMORE - WATFORD (17 miles).
      LONDON The Bull, Holborn   dep. 3 00 p.m.
      WATFORD   dep. 9 00 a.m.
          Journey time: 2½ hours

3549 (4-8) B.W. Horne & Co.

LONDON - BARNET - ST. ALBANS - DUNSTABLE - WOBURN - NEWPORT
PAGNELL - OLNEY - WELLINGBOROUGH (70 miles).
        LONDON George & Blue Boar, Holborn dep. 8 00 a.m, Mon., Wed., Fri.
        WELLINGBOROUGH   dep.   Tu., Th., Sat.
        Journey time : 9 hours

4758 (4-11) B.W. Horne & Co.
        'THE NORFOLK HERO'
LONDON - WOODFORD - EPPING - SAWBRIDGEWORTH - BISHOPS STORTFORD -
GREAT CHESTERFORD - CAMBRIDGE - NEWMARKET - MILDENHALL - BRANDON -
SWAFFHAM - FAKENHAM - WALSINGHAM - WELLS (130 miles).
        LONDON Golden Cross, Charing Cross dep. 6 00 a.m. Mon., Wed., Fri.
        WELLS   dep. 6 00 a.m. Tu., Th., Sat.
        Journey time: 15 hours

3525 (4-8) J. Kershaw
        'KERSHAW'S COACH'
LONDON - BARNET - HATFIELD - WELWYN (25 miles).
        LONDON Three Cups, Aldersgate Street dep. 2 30 p.m.
        WELWYN   dep. 7 00 a.m. Mon. & Fri.
        dep. 10 00 a.m. Tu, Wed, Th., Sa.
        Journey time : 3½ hours

417 (12-3) A. Mills
        An Omnibus
LONDON - BROMLEY - WESTERHAM (24 miles).
        LONDON Green Man & Still, Oxford Street dep.   Tu.
        WESTERHAM   dep. 7 00 a.m. Mon.
        Journey time :

2255 (4-8) R. Gray & Co.

LONDON - KINGSTON - ESHER - WEYBRIDGE (23 miles).
        LONDON Bolt-in-Tun, Fleet Street dep. 3 30 p.m.
        WEYBRIDGE   dep.
        Journey time: 3 hours

2137(4-8),2187(4-11) W.L. Dore & Co./S.A. Mountain & Co.
'THE MAGNET'
LONDON-HOUNSLOW-STAINES-EGHAM-BAGSHOT-CAMBERLEY-
HARTLEY WINTNEY-BASINGSTOKE-WHITCHURCH-ANDOVER-
SALISBURY-BLANDFORD-DORCHESTER-WEYMOUTH (130 miles).

LONDON Belle Sauvage, Ludgate Hill and
Saracens Head, Snow Hill dep. 5 00 a.m.
WEYMOUTH   dep.
Journey time: 15 hours

4956,4957 (4-11) J. Hazell & Co.
'THE BLUE'
LONDON-ILFORD-ROMFORD-BRENTWOOD-CHELMSFORD-COLCHESTER-
IPSWICH-WOODBRIDGE-WICKHAM MARKET (83 miles).

LONDON Belle Sauvage, Ludgate Hill dep. 11 30 a.m.
WICKHAM MARKET   dep. 7 15 a.m.
Journey time: 11 hours

2004,2054,2170(4-11) R. Gray & Co./R. Fagg & Co./H. Thumwood
UNION COACHES
LONDON-HOUNSLOW-SLOUGH-WINDSOR (25 miles).

LONDON Bolt-in-Tun, Fleet Street dep. 7 00 a.m.
White Bear, Basinghall Street dep.   8 00 a.m.
Cross Keys, Wood Street dep.   4 00 p.m.
WINDSOR   dep.
Journey time: 3½ hours

2140,2204(4-8), 2262(4-11) T. Peer

LONDON-HOUNSLOW-SLOUGH-WINDSOR (25 miles).
LONDON Saracens Head, Friday Street dep. 8 00 a.m., 4 00, 5 00 p.m.
WINDSOR   dep.
Journey time: 3½ hours

2006,2007(4-11) J. Moody

LONDON-HOUNSLOW-SLOUGH-WINDSOR (25 miles).

LONDON Cross Keys, Wood Street and
Belle Sauvage, Ludgate Hill dep. 8 00 a.m., 2 00 p.m.
WINDSOR   dep.
Journey time: 3½ hours

2035 (12-3) G. Burgess
An Omnibus
LONDON-HOUNSLOW-SLOUGH-WINDSOR (25 miles).
      LONDON Bank   dep.
      WINDSOR   dep.
        Journey time:

4386 (4-11) W. Ekin & Co.
'THE WISBECH DAY COACH'
LONDON-WALTHAM CROSS-HODDESDON-WARE-PUCKERIDGE-
BUNTINGFORD-ROYSTON-CAMBRIDGE-ST.IVES-SOMERSHAM-
CHATTERIS-MARCH-WISBECH (94 miles).
    LONDON Belle Sauvage, Ludgate Hill dep. 7·30 a.m. Tu., Th., Sat.
    WISBECH   dep. 7·00 a.m. Mon., Wed., Fri.
        Journey time: 11½ hours

4461 (4-11) B.W. Horne & Co.
'THE DEFIANCE'
LONDON-WALTHAM CROSS-HODDESDON-WARE-PUCKERIDGE-
BUNTINGFORD-ROYSTON-CAMBRIDGE-ST.IVES-SOMERSHAM-
CHATTERIS-MARCH-WISBECH (97 miles).
    LONDON Golden Cross, Charing Cross dep. 7·30 a.m. Mon., Wed., Fri.
    WISBECH   dep. 7·00 a.m. Tu., Th., Sat.
        Journey time: 11½ hours

2914, 2915 (4-11) E. Sherman & Co.
'THE SOVEREIGN'
LONDON-EALING-UXBRIDGE-HIGH WYCOMBE-OXFORD-
WOODSTOCK-CHIPPING NORTON-MORETON-IN-MARSH-BROADWAY
EVESHAM-PERSHORE-WORCESTER (113 miles).
    LONDON Bull & Mouth, St. Martin's-le-Grand dep. 5·30 a.m.
    WORCESTER   dep.
        Journey time: 12½ hours

2923, 2956 (4-11) E. Sherman & Co.
'THE TELEGRAPH'
LONDON-EALING-UXBRIDGE-HIGH WYCOMBE-OXFORD-
WOODSTOCK-CHIPPING NORTON-MORETON-IN-MARSH-BROADWAY
EVESHAM-PERSHORE-WORCESTER (113 miles).
    LONDON Bull & Mouth, St. Martin's-le-Grand dep. 4·30 p.m.
    WORCESTER   dep.
        Journey time: 15 hours

2941, 2964 (4-11) W. Gilbert & Co.
'THE PAUL PRY'
LONDON - EALING - UXBRIDGE - HIGH WYCOMBE - OXFORD - WITNEY - CHELTENHAM - TEWKESBURY - WORCESTER (122 miles).

LONDON Blossoms Inn, Lawrence Lane dep. 4 45p.m.
WORCESTER   dep.
Journey time:

1358, 1359 (4-11) W. Chaplin & Co.
An Accommodation Coach
LONDON - MORDEN - EPSOM - LEATHERHEAD - DORKING - HORSHAM - WASHINGTON - WORTHING (57 miles).

LONDON White Horse, Fetter Lane dep. 8 30 a.m.
WORTHING   dep. 9 00 a.m.
Journey time: 7½ hours

1384, 1385 (4-11) W. Chaplin & Co.
'THE SOVEREIGN'
LONDON - MORDEN - EPSOM - LEATHERHEAD - DORKING - HORSHAM - WASHINGTON - WORTHING (57 miles).

LONDON White Horse, Fetter Lane dep. 10 00a.m.
WORTHING   dep. 10 00 a.m.
Journey time: 5½ hours

4929, 4933 (4-11) E. Sherman & Co.
'THE TELEGRAPH'
LONDON - ILFORD - ROMFORD - BRENTWOOD - CHELMSFORD - COLCHESTER - IPSWICH - WOODBRIDGE - WICKHAM MARKET - SAXMUNDHAM - LOWESTOFT - YARMOUTH (127 miles).

LONDON Green Man & Still, Oxford Street dep. 6 30 p.m.
YARMOUTH   dep. 5 00 p.m.
Journey time: 15 hours

4934, 4935 (4-11) W. Chaplin & Co.
'THE STAR'
LONDON - ILFORD - ROMFORD - BRENTWOOD - CHELMSFORD - COLCHESTER - IPSWICH - WOODBRIDGE - WICKHAM MARKET - SAXMUNDHAM - LOWESTOFT - YARMOUTH (127 miles).

LONDON White Horse, Fetter Lane dep. 6 30 a.m.
YARMOUTH   dep. 7 00 a.m.
Journey time: 15 hours

3533,3534,3536,3537(4-5) S.A. Mountain & Co.

'THE ROYAL EXPRESS'

LONDON - BARNET - HATFIELD - STEVENAGE - BALDOCK -
BIGGLESWADE - EATON SOCON - NORMAN CROSS - STAMFORD -
GRANTHAM - NEWARK - RETFORD - BAWTRY - DONCASTER -
SELBY - YORK (200 miles).

    LONDON Saracens Head, Snow Hill   dep. 7 30 a.m.
    YORK   dep. 9 00 a.m.
            Journey time: 24 hours

4368,4369,4404(4-8) W. Chaplin & Co.

'THE HIGHFLYER'

★ LONDON - WALTHAM CROSS - HODDESDON - HERTFORD - STEVENAGE -
BALDOCK - BIGGLESWADE - EATON SOCON - NORMAN CROSS -
STAMFORD - GRANTHAM - NEWARK - RETFORD - BAWTRY -
DONCASTER - SELBY - YORK (203 miles).

    LONDON White Horse, Fetter Lane   dep. 8 00 a.m.
    YORK   dep. 5 00 a.m.
            Journey time: 24 hours

★ Section of route London - Edinburgh. The service between York
and Edinburgh provided by proprietor at Newcastle upon Tyne.

5003, 5004 (6-12) J. Nelson & Co.

'THE SHANNON'

LONDON - ILFORD - ROMFORD - BRENTWOOD - CHELMSFORD - COLCHESTER -
IPSWICH - WOODBRIDGE - WICKHAM MARKET - SAXMUNDHAM - YOXFORD
(93 miles).

        LONDON The Bull, Aldgate dep. 7 45 a.m.
        YOXFORD   dep. 6 30 a.m.
            Journey time: 12 hours

TABLE 1A

ADDITIONAL COACHES
FROM AND TO LONDON

SERVICE MILES	PROPRIETOR	COACHES	FREQUENCY
LONDON (Bull & Mouth, St. Martin's-le-Grand) & BIRMINGHAM			
111	E. Sherman & Co.	3503, 3504 (4-11)	I ret. jny. daily
109	E. Sherman & Co.	3430, 3431 (4-8)	I ret. jny. Mon.-Sat.
LONDON (Golden Cross, Charing Cross) & BIRMINGHAM			
111	B.W. Horne & Co.	3556, 3557 (4-11)	I ret. jny. daily
LONDON (Yorkshire Stingo, Paddington) & BRIGHTON			
54	J. Rickman & Co.	1297, 1298 (4-11)	I ret. jny. Mon.-Sat.
55	Roberts & Co.	1284, 1473 (4-11)	I ret. jny. Mon.-Sat.
LONDON (Knightsbridge) & BRIGHTON			
54	H.J. Taylor	1404, 1409 (4-8)	I ret. jny. Mon.-Sat.
LONDON (Golden Cross, Charing Cross) & BROMPTON			
32½	J. Edwards & Co.	487 (4-5)	I ret. jny. daily
LONDON (Golden Cross, Charing Cross) & BURY ST. EDMUNDS			
77	B.W. Horne & Co.	4769, 4770 (4-8)	I ret. jny. daily
76	E. Sherman & Co.	4756, 4757 (4-11)	I ret. jny. Mon.-Sat.
LONDON (Gloster Warehouse, Oxford Street) & CANTERBURY			
57	B.W. Horne & Co.	611, 612 (4-11)	I ret. jny. daily
LONDON (Golden Cross, Charing Cross) & CANTERBURY			
56	B.W. Horne & Co.	605 (4-8)	I ret. jny. daily
57	B.W. Horne & Co.	610 (4-8)	4 jnys. per week
LONDON (220 Piccadilly) & CHELMSFORD			
32	W. Woods & Co.	4981 (4-8)	I ret. jny. Mon.-Sat.
LONDON (Cross Keys, Wood Street) & CHOBHAM			
29	G. Chalmers	1910 (4-8)	I ret. jny. Mon.-Sat.
LONDON (The Bull, Aldgate) & COLCHESTER			
51	J. Nelson & Co.	4947, 4948 (4-11)	I ret. jny. daily
LONDON (Black Lion, Water Lane) & ESHER			
17	E. Mills & Co.	2030 (4-8)	I ret. jny. Mon.-Sat.
LONDON (Golden Cross, Charing Cross) & FARNINGHAM			
19	E. Hollands	405 (4-11)	I ret. jny. Mon.-Sat.
LONDON (St. Pauls) & HARLINGTON Middlesex			
17	H. Limpus	1946 (6-9)	I ret. jny. daily

LONDON (Bolt in Tun, Fleet Street) & HERSHAM GREEN			
17½	W. Bennett & Co.	2010 (4-8)	1 ret. jny. Mon.–Sat.
LONDON (George & Blue Boar, Holborn) & HERTFORD			
23	J. Staples & Co.	4300 (4-8)	1 ret. jny. Mon.–Sat.
LONDON (The Bull, Aldgate) & IPSWICH			
69	J. Nelson & Co.	5012 (4-11)	1 sgl. jny. daily
LONDON (Spread Eagle, Gracechurch Street) & IPSWICH			
69	W. Chaplin & Co.	5013 (4-11)	1 sgl. jny. daily
LONDON (Bell & Crown, Holborn) & LINCOLN			
132	R. Fagg & Co.	4376 (4-8)	1 sgl. jny. Mon.–Sat.
LONDON (White Horse, Fetter Lane) & LINCOLN			
133	W. Chaplin & Co.	3511 (4-8)	1 sgl. jny. Mon.–Sat.
LONDON (Belle Sauvage, Ludgate Hill) & LINCOLN			
133	J. Bryant	3450, 3495 (4-5)	1 ret. jny. Mon.–Sat.
LONDON (Golden Cross, Charing Cross) & LYNN			
101	B. W. Horne & Co.	4402 (4-11)	1 sgl. jny. Mon.–Sat.
LONDON (Belle Sauvage, Ludgate Hill) & MAIDENHEAD			
28¼	R. Lovegrove	2000 (4-8)	1 ret. jny. Mon.–Sat.
LONDON (Golden Cross, Charing Cross) & MAIDSTONE			
36	B. W. Horne & Co.	474, 475 (4-11)	1 ret. jny. Mon.–Sat.
LONDON (Regent Circus, Piccadilly) & MAIDSTONE			
36	T. Collis & Co.	509 (4-8)	1 ret. jny. Mon.–Sat.
LONDON (Saracens Head, Snow Hill) & MARLBOROUGH			
76	S. A. Mountain & Co.	2171 (4-11)	1 sgl. jny. Mon.–Sat.
LONDON (Regent Circus, Piccadilly) & NOTTINGHAM			
126	B. W. Horne & Co.	3487, 3502 (4-5)	1 ret. jny. daily
LONDON (Belle Sauvage, Ludgate Hill) & PORTSMOUTH			
72	G. Vicat & Co.	1957 (4-8)	1 sgl. jny. Mon.–Sat.
LONDON (Belle Sauvage, Ludgate Hill) & READING			
41	J. Houlton & Co.	2016 (4-8)	1 ret. jny. Mon.–Sat.
LONDON (Black Lion, Water Lane) & READING			
41	T. Williams & Co.	2023, 2055 (4-11)	1 ret. jny. Mon.–Sat.
LONDON (Blue Boar, Aldgate) & ROCHFORD			
40	J. Thorogood	4925 (4-8)	1 ret. jny. Mon.–Sat.
LONDON (The Bull, Aldgate) & SAFFRON WALDEN			
42	W. Lowe & Co.	4966 (4-11)	1 ret. jny. Mon. only
LONDON (The Greyhound, Smithfield) & ST. ALBANS			
22	E. Reeves	3120 (4-8)	1 ret. jny. Mon.–Sat.
LONDON (Belle Sauvage, Ludgate Hill & STAINES			
19	J. Moore	2146 (4-8)	1 ret. jny. daily

LONDON (Boar & Castle, Oxford Street) & STANMORE			
11	M. Sanderson & Co.	3101 (4-8)	1 ret. jny. daily

LONDON (Old Bell, Holborn) & SUNNINGHILL			
25	R. Fagg & Co.	2128 (4-11)	1 ret. jny. Mon.–Sat.

LONDON (Cross Keys, Wood Street) & WANTAGE			
62	B. W. Horne & Co.	1998 (4-5)	1 sgl. jny. Mon.–Sat.

LONDON (Black Lion, Water Lane) & WANTAGE			
62	S. Williams & Co.	2005, 2071 (4-8)	1 ret. jny. Mon.–Sat.

LONDON (Bell & Crown, Holborn) & WARE			
23	R. Fagg & Co.	4396 (4-8)	1 ret. jny. Mon. & Fri.

LONDON (Belle Sauvage, Ludgate Hill) & WELLS Norfolk			
124	R. Nelson & Co.	4768 (4-8)	1 sgl. jny. Mon.–Sat.

LONDON (Bolt in Tun, Fleet Street) & WISBECH			
96	R. Gray & Co.	4389 (4-8)	1 sgl. jny. Mon.–Sat.

TABLE 1B

BRANCH COACHES IN LONDON

working mainly between West End and City, and also between West End and Elephant & Castle, in connection with Long-Distance Coaches

ESTABLISHMENT	PROPRIETOR	COACH
SWAN WITH TWO NECKS, LAD LANE	R. Edwards	150 (4-5)
"	W. Chaplin & Co.	201 (4-5)
"	"	202 (4-5)
"	"	204 (4-5)
BULL & MOUTH, ST. MARTIN'S-LE-GRAND	E. Sherman & Co.	190 (4-5)
BELL & CROWN, HOLBORN	R. Fagg & Co.	207 (4-5)
BELLE SAUVAGE, LUDGATE HILL	R. Nelson	219 (4-5)
"	"	319 (4-5)
BLOSSOMS INN, LAWRENCE LANE	W. Gilbert	273 (4-5)
"	"	302 (4-5)
GOLDEN CROSS, CHARING CROSS	B. W. Horne & Co.	306 (4-5)
"	"	307 (4-5)

TABLE 1C

DETAILS OF:

(a) THE PRINCIPAL PROPRIETORS OF LONG-DISTANCE STAGE & ROYAL MAIL COACHES FROM & TO LONDON;
(b) NUMBER OF COACHES ON LEASE OR OWNED;
(c) PRINCIPAL COACHING ESTABLISHMENTS.

WILLIAM JAMES CHAPLIN (106)
SWAN WITH TWO NECKS, LAD LANE
SPREAD EAGLE, GRACECHURCH STREET
WHITE HORSE, FETTER LANE

BENJAMIN WORTHY HORNE (92)
GOLDEN CROSS, CHARING CROSS
CROSS KEYS, WOOD STREET
GEORGE & BLUE BOAR, HOLBORN
THE BULL, HOLBORN
OLD BELL, HOLBORN

EDWARD SHERMAN (77)
BULL & MOUTH, ST. MARTIN'S-LE-GRAND

ROBERT NELSON (53)
BELLE SAUVAGE, LUDGATE HILL

ROBERT GRAY (29)
BOLT IN TUN, FLEET STREET

ROBERT FAGG (28)
BELL & CROWN, HOLBORN
WHITE BEAR, BASINGHALL STREET

JOHN NELSON (23)
THE BULL, ALDGATE

SARAH ANN MOUNTAIN (21)
SARACENS HEAD, SNOW HILL

WILLIAM GILBERT (21)
BLOSSOMS INN, LAWRENCE LANE

JAMES HEARN (16)
KINGS ARMS, SNOW HILL

TABLE 1D

NUMBER OF DAILY DEPARTURES OF LONG-DISTANCE STAGE & ROYAL MAIL COACHES FROM PRINCIPAL ESTABLISHMENTS IN LONDON

BULL & MOUTH, ST. MARTIN'S-LE-GRAND	30
BELLE SAUVAGE, LUDGATE HILL	29
GOLDEN CROSS, CHARING CROSS	28
SPREAD EAGLE, GRACECHURCH STREET	26
SWAN WITH TWO NECKS, LAD LANE	23
BOLT IN TUN, FLEET STREET	20
THE BULL, ALDGATE	16
THE BULL, HOLBORN	11
GEORGE & BLUE BOAR, HOLBORN	11
WHITE HORSE, FETTER LANE	11
CROSS KEYS, WOOD STREET	10
KINGS ARMS, SNOW HILL	10
BLOSSOMS INN, LAWRENCE LANE	9
BELL & CROWN, HOLBORN	7
OLD BELL, HOLBORN	7
SARACENS HEAD, SNOW HILL	6
WHITE BEAR, BASINGHALL STREET	5
	259

NOTES

(a) Total number of coaches leaving London for country places each day :— 342

(b) Figures apply to Weekdays. Departures considerably reduced on Sundays

TABLE 1E
OTHER COACHING ESTABLISHMENTS IN LONDON

Terminals and Calling Points for Long-Distance and Local Coaches

AXE, ALDERMANBURY
GEORGE, ALDERMANBURY
CASTLE & FALCON, ALDERSGATE
THREE CUPS, ALDERSGATE
THREE NUNS, ALDERSGATE
WHITE BEAR, ALDERSGATE
BLUE BOAR, ALDGATE
SARACENS HEAD, ALDGATE
THREE NUNS, ALDGATE
—   BAKER STREET
COFFEE HOUSE, BANK
GERRARDS HALL, BASING LANE
—   BILLITER SQUARE
BULL, BISHOPSGATE
FLOWER POT, BISHOPSGATE
FOUR SWANS, BISHOPSGATE
GREEN DRAGON, BISHOPSGATE
KINGS ARMS, BISHOPSGATE
VINE, BISHOPSGATE
CATHERINE WHEEL, BOROUGH
GEORGE, BOROUGH
HALF MOON, BOROUGH
NAGS HEAD, BOROUGH
QUEENS HEAD, BOROUGH
SPUR, BOROUGH
HORSE SHOE & MAGPIE, BRIDGE STREET
SHEPHERD'S WAREHOUSE, CAMOMILE STREET
SHIP, CHARING CROSS
SILVER CROSS, CHARING CROSS

BRITISH COFFEE HOUSE, COCKSPUR STREET
— CORNHILL
— COVENTRY STREET
— EASTCHEAP
KINGS & KEY, FLEET STREET
SARACENS HEAD, FRIDAY STREET
4 GRACECHURCH STREET
8 GRACECHURCH STREET
CROSS KEYS, GRACECHURCH STREET
GEORGE & GATE, GRACECHURCH STREET
HALF MOON, GRACECHURCH STREET
PEWTER PLATTER, GRACECHURCH STREET
UNION OFFICE, 11 GRACECHURCH STREET
GREYHOUND, HOLBORN
BLUE POSTS, HOLBORN BRIDGE
— INDIA HOUSE
PEACOCK, ISLINGTON
PRICE'S, ISLINGTON
— KINGS CROSS
— KNIGHTSBRIDGE
BLACK BOY & CAMEL, LEADENHALL STREET
BULL, LEADENHALL STREET
HERCULES, LEADENHALL STREET
KINGS ARMS, LEADENHALL STREET
LAMB, LEADENHALL STREET
CLEMMITT'S INN, OLD BAILEY
NEW INN, OLD BAILEY
KINGS HEAD, OLD CHANGE
NEW INN, OLD CHANGE
335 OXFORD STREET
336 OXFORD STREET
BOAR & CASTLE, 6 OXFORD STREET
GLOSTER WAREHOUSE, OXFORD STREET
GREEN MAN & STILL, 122 OXFORD STREET
YORKSHIRE STINGO, PADDINGTON
52 PICCADILLY
220 PICCADILLY
BLACK BEAR, PICCADILLY
GLOUCESTER COFFEE HOUSE, PICCADILLY

NEW WHITE HORSE CELLAR, PICCADILLY
OLD WHITE HORSE CELLAR, PICCADILLY
REGENT CIRCUS, PICCADILLY
SPREAD EAGLE OFFICE, PICCADILLY
WHITE BEAR, 221 PICCADILLY
— PORTMAN STREET
— ROYAL EXCHANGE
ANGEL, ST. CLEMENTS
NAGS HEAD, ST. JAMES STREET
GOLDEN LION, ST. JOHN STREET
WINDMILL, ST. JOHN STREET
CROWN, ST. PAULS CHURCHYARD
GOOSE & GRIDIRON, ST. PAULS CHURCHYARD
GREYHOUND, SMITHFIELD
RAM, SMITHFIELD
ROSE, SMITHFIELD
— SOMERSET HOUSE
HUNGERFORD OFFICE, 16 STRAND
RED LION, STRAND
SPOTTED DOG, STRAND
WHITE HART, STRAND
BLUE POSTS, TOTTENHAM COURT ROAD
BLACK LION, WATER LANE

TABLE 2

TIMETABLES

OF

ROYAL MAIL COACHES

FROM & TO

LONDON

LONDON & DOVER　　　　　ROYAL MAIL
B.W. Horne & Co.

7 30 p.m.	LONDON Golden Cross, Charing Cross	6 26 ↑
8 00	LONDON General Post Office	6 11
10 00	DARTFORD	4 11
11 45 ↓	ROCHESTER	2 34
1 05 a.m.	SITTINGBOURNE	1 17 a.m.
3 01	CANTERBURY	11 25 ↑
4 57 ↓	DOVER	9 45 p.m. ↑

LONDON & HASTINGS　　　ROYAL MAIL
R. Gray & Co.

7 30 p.m.	LONDON Bolt in Tun, Fleet Street	6 20 ↑
8 00	LONDON General Post Office	6 05
11 05 ↓	SEVENOAKS	3 00
12 34 a.m.	TUNBRIDGE WELLS	1 35 a.m.
2 29	ROBERTSBRIDGE	11 38 ↑
3 11	BATTLE	10 56
4 15	HASTINGS	9 42
4 37 ↓	ST. LEONARDS	9 30 p.m.

LONDON & BRIGHTON　　　ROYAL MAIL
W. Gilbert & Co.

7 30 p.m.	LONDON Blossoms Inn, Lawrence Lane	6 10 ↑
8 00	LONDON General Post Office	5 55
9 45	CROYDON	4 10
11 10 ↓	REIGATE	2 48
12 20 a.m.	CRAWLEY	1 38
1 30	CUCKFIELD	12 23 a.m.
3 20 ↓	BRIGHTON	10 30 p.m.

LONDON & PORTSMOUTH   ROYAL MAIL
W. Chaplin & Co./ R. Gray & Co.

7 30 p.m.	LONDON White Horse, Fetter Lane/ Bolt in Tun, Fleet Street	6 45 ↑
8 00	LONDON General Post Office	6 30
9 35 ↓	KINGSTON	4 55
12 35 a.m.	MOUSEHILL	1 55 a.m.
2 55	PETERSFIELD	11 40 ↑
5 10 ↓	PORTSMOUTH	9 30 p.m.

LONDON & POOLE   ROYAL MAIL
W. Chaplin & Co.

7 30 p.m.	LONDON Swan with Two Necks, Lad Lane	6 40 ↑
8 00	LONDON General Post Office	6 25
10 05 ↓	STAINES	4 20
12 22 a.m.	FARNHAM	2 08
1 22	ALTON	1 08 a.m.
4 30	SOUTHAMPTON	9 18 ↑
7 26	RINGWOOD	6 52
9 18 ↓	POOLE	5 00 p.m.

LONDON & EXETER   ROYAL MAIL
W. Chaplin & Co./ R. Fagg & Co.

7 30 p.m.	LONDON Swan with Two Necks, Lad Lane/ Bell & Crown, Holborn	5 57 ↑
8 00	LONDON General Post Office	5 42
9 56 ↓	STAINES	3 46 a.m.
2 42 a.m.	ANDOVER	11 00 ↑
4 27	SALISBURY	8 50
6 41	SHAFTESBURY	6 48
8 53	YEOVIL	4 30
10 12 ↓	CREWKERNE	3 40
11 00	CHARD	2 55
12 31 p.m.	HONITON	1 27 p.m.
2 12 ↓	EXETER	11 50 a.m.

LONDON – EXETER – FALMOUTH – PENZANCE
ROYAL MAIL
E. Sherman & Co.

7 30 p.m.	LONDON Bull & Mouth, St. Martin's-le-Grand	6 49 ↑
8 00	LONDON General Post Office	6 34
10 02	STAINES	4 32
11 00 ↓	BAGSHOT	3 33
12 10 a.m.	HARTFORD BRIDGE	2 33
1 55	OVERTON	12 48 a.m.
3 02	ANDOVER	11 32 ↑
4 52	SALISBURY	9 32
7 19	BLANDFORD	7 09
8 57	DORCHESTER	5 02
10 53 ↓	BRIDPORT	3 20
12 17 p.m.	AXMINSTER	1 53
1 21	HONITON	12 51 p.m.
2 59 ↓	EXETER	11 13 a.m.
5 00 p.m.	EXETER	9 15 ↑
7 17	OKEHAMPTON	6 58
9 23	LAUNCESTON	4 47
11 53 ↓	BODMIN	2 07 a.m.
2 40 a.m.	TRURO	11 12 ↑
3 55 ↓	FALMOUTH	10 00 p.m.
6 00 a.m.	FALMOUTH	8 20 ↑
9 20 ↓	PENZANCE	5 00 p.m.

LONDON & FALMOUTH   ROYAL MAIL
W. Chaplin & Co.

7 30 p.m.	LONDON Swan with Two Necks, Lad Lane	7 05 ↑
8 00	LONDON General Post Office	6 50
10 47 ↓	BAGSHOT	4 02
1 41 a.m.	WHITCHURCH	1 08
2 20	ANDOVER	12 19 a.m.
3 39	AMESBURY	11 00 ↑
7 50	ILCHESTER	6 49
9 23	ILMINSTER	5 41
11 00 ↓	HONITON	4 04
12 34 p.m.	EXETER	2 20
2 41	ASHBURTON	12 03 p.m.
5 05	PLYMOUTH	9 39 ↑
5 14	DEVONPORT	9 30
7 55	LISKEARD	6 52
9 12	LOSTWITHIEL	5 36
10 20	ST. AUSTELL	4 29
11 55 ↓	TRURO	2 55
1 05 a.m.	FALMOUTH	1 45 a.m.

LONDON – BATH – DEVONPORT   ROYAL MAIL
W. Chaplin & Co.

7 30 p.m.	LONDON Swan with Two Necks, Lad Lane	6 51
8 00	LONDON General Post Office	6 36
9 12	HOUNSLOW	5 26
10 40	MAIDENHEAD	3 44
1 53 a.m.	NEWBURY	12 42 a.m.
3 43	MARLBOROUGH	10 49
5 06	DEVIZES	9 24
7 00	BATH	7 30 p.m.

7 30 a.m.	BATH	7 00
8 50	OLD DOWN	5 35
9 27	WELLS	4 55
11 30	BRIDGEWATER	2 52
12 35 p.m.	TAUNTON	1 37 p.m.
2 42	COLLUMPTON	11 38
3 57	EXETER	10 15
5 55	CHUDLEIGH	9 02
6 33	NEWTON ABBOT	8 25
7 25	TOTNES	7 30
10 05	DEVONPORT	4 45 a.m.

LONDON – BRISTOL – PEMBROKE   ROYAL MAIL
W. Chaplin & Co.

7 30 p.m.	LONDON Swan with Two Necks, Lad Lane	7 14
8 00	LONDON General Post Office	6 59
9 12	HOUNSLOW	5 47
10 50	MAIDENHEAD	4 05
1 41 a.m.	NEWBURY	1 10 a.m.
4 49	CALNE	10 02
6 32	BATH	8 15
7 45	BRISTOL	7 00 p.m.

8 00 a.m.	BRISTOL	6 21
9 12	NEW PASSAGE FERRY	5 09
12 53 p.m.	CARDIFF	1 28 p.m.
5 18	SWANSEA	8 38
8 31	CARMARTHEN	5 45
10 51	COLDBLOW	3 30
12 34 a.m.	HOBBS POINT	1 47
1 09	PEMBROKE	1 12 a.m.

LONDON & STROUD   ROYAL MAIL
W. Chaplin & Co./ B.W. Horne & Co.

7 30 p.m.	LONDON Swan with Two Necks, Lad Lane/ Golden Cross, Charing Cross	6 52
8 00	LONDON General Post Office	6 37
11 13	MAIDENHEAD	3 24
12 14 a.m.	HENLEY	2 28
1 27	BENSON	1 10
2 27	ABINGDON	12 10 a.m.
3 57	FARINGDON	10 40
5 02	FAIRFORD	9 35
5 57	CIRENCESTER	8 35
7 47	STROUD	6 50 p.m.

LONDON – GLOUCESTER – CARMARTHEN   ROYAL MAIL
B.W. Horne & Co.

7 30 p.m.	LONDON Golden Cross, Charing Cross	7 05 ↑
8 00	LONDON General Post Office	6 50
9 20	HOUNSLOW	5 30
11 08 ↓	MAIDENHEAD	3 49
2 38 a.m.	OXFORD	12 19 a.m.
3 58	WITNEY	11 00 ↑
5 43	NORTHLEACH	9 16
7 03	CHELTENHAM	7 57
8 00 ↓	GLOUCESTER	7 00 p.m.
8 15 a.m.	GLOUCESTER	6 45 ↑
10 08	ROSS	4 52
11 11 ↓	MONMOUTH	3 44
12 53 p.m.	ABERGAVENNY	2 02 p.m.
3 01	BRECON	11 54 ↑
5 22	LLANDOVERY	9 48
6 32	LLANDILO	8 33
8 00 ↓	CARMARTHEN	7 10 a.m.

LONDON – WORCESTER – LUDLOW   ROYAL MAIL
E. Sherman & Co.

7 30 p.m.	LONDON Bull & Mouth, St. Martin's-le-Grand	6 40 ↑
8 00	LONDON General Post Office	6 25
11 25 ↓	HIGH WYCOMBE	3 00
2 07 a.m.	OXFORD	12 07 a.m.
5 05	MORETON-IN-MARSH	9 07 ↑
8 20 ↓	WORCESTER	5 45 p.m.
9 20 a.m.	WORCESTER	4 49 ↑
11 27 ↓	TENBURY	2 42
12 24 p.m.	LUDLOW	1 45 p.m.

LONDON – BIRMINGHAM – STOURPORT ROYAL MAIL
J. Hearn & Co.

7 30 p.m.	LONDON Kings Arms, Snow Hill	7 11
8 00	LONDON General Post Office	6 56
12 15 a.m.	AYLESBURY	2 41
1 57	BICESTER	12 59 a.m.
3 30	BANBURY	11 26
4 55	SOUTHAM	10 01
5 52	WARWICK	9 04
7 56	BIRMINGHAM	7 00 p.m.
8 15 a.m.	BIRMINGHAM	6 40
10 22	KIDDERMINSTER	4 24
11 03	STOURPORT	3 43 p.m.

LONDON & HOLYHEAD   ROYAL MAIL
W. Chaplin & Co.

7 30 p.m.	LONDON Swan with Two Necks, Lad Lane	7 15
8 00	LONDON General Post Office	7 00
1 26 a.m.	STONY STRATFORD	1 34
2 12	TOWCESTER	12 49 a.m.
3 25	DAVENTRY	11 32
4 11	DUNCHURCH	10 51
5 18	COVENTRY	9 46
7 08	BIRMINGHAM	7 31
9 01	WOLVERHAMPTON	6 14
10 14	SHIFNAL	5 01
11 59	SHREWSBURY	3 01
1 45 p.m.	OSWESTRY	1 17
2 57	LLANGOLLEN	12 13 p.m.
3 57	CORWEN	11 13
6 21	BETTWS-Y-COED	8 49
7 02	CAPEL CURIG	8 08
8 20	BANGOR	6 50
10 55	HOLYHEAD	4 15 a.m.

LONDON & LIVERPOOL   ROYAL MAIL
W. Chaplin & Co.

7 30 p.m.	LONDON Swan with Two Necks, Lad Lane	7 00
8 00	LONDON General Post Office	6 45
10 44	REDBOURN	4 01
1 26 a.m.	STONY STRATFORD	1 09
2 12	TOWCESTER	12 22 a.m.
3 25	DAVENTRY	11 09
4 11	DUNCHURCH	10 23
5 18	COVENTRY	9 16
6 31	COLESHILL	8 03
8 02	LICHFIELD	6 03
10 41	STONE	3 53
11 33	NEWCASTLE-UNDER-LYME	3 01
1 52 p.m.	KNUTSFORD	12 43 p.m.
3 00	WARRINGTON	11 35
4 50	LIVERPOOL	9 45 a.m.

LONDON & WOODSIDE (for Liverpool)   ROYAL MAIL
B. W. Horne & Co.

7 30 p.m.	LONDON Golden Cross, Charing Cross	7 09
8 00	LONDON General Post Office	6 54
11 34	DUNSTABLE	3 20
12 31 a.m.	WOBURN	2 07 a.m.
3 31	NORTHAMPTON	11 27
5 30	LUTTERWORTH	9 01
6 36	HINCKLEY	7 45
7 51	ATHERSTONE	6 57
8 24	TAMWORTH	6 04
9 26	LICHFIELD	5 02
11 11	STAFFORD	3 07
1 23 p.m.	WOORE	1 05
2 16	NANTWICH	12 12 p.m.
3 13	TARPORLEY	11 17
4 16	CHESTER	10 10
5 54	WOODSIDE	8 40 a.m.

LONDON – MANCHESTER – PORT PATRICK   ROYAL MAIL
W. Chaplin & Co.

7 30 p.m.	LONDON Swan with Two Necks, Lad Lane	6 41
8 00	LONDON General Post Office	6 26
10 44	REDBOURN	3 42
11 32	DUNSTABLE	2 50
12 27 a.m.	WOBURN	1 52 a.m.
2 45	NORTHAMPTON	11 18
4 37	MARKET HARBOROUGH	9 28
6 03	LEICESTER	7 38
7 30	LOUGHBOROUGH	6 31
8 04	KEGWORTH	5 53
9 07	DERBY	4 20
10 25	ASHBOURNE	2 58 p.m.
1 13 p.m.	MACCLESFIELD	11 56
2 03	BULLOCKS SMITHY	11 00
3 00	MANCHESTER	10 00 a.m.
4 30 p.m.	MANCHESTER	7 07
7 30	PRESTON	4 07
9 53	LANCASTER	1 51
10 56	BURTON IN KENDAL	12 44 a.m.
12 04 a.m.	KENDAL	11 35
1 57	SHAP	9 42
3 00	PENRITH	8 28
4 53	CARLISLE	6 30
7 20	ANNAN	6 18 / 3 43 p.m.
9 03	DUMFRIES	4 35
11 39	CASTLE DOUGLAS	2 59
1 24 p.m.	GATEHOUSE	1 14 a.m.
3 33	NEWTON STEWART	11 05
6 00	GLENLUCE	9 08
8 08	PORT PATRICK	7 00 p.m.

Times on the southbound journey between Port Patrick and Carlisle subject to confirmation

LONDON & HALIFAX — ROYAL MAIL
B.W. Horne & Co.

7 30 p.m.	LONDON Golden Cross, Charing Cross	7 02
8 00	LONDON General Post Office	6 47
12 12 a.m.	WOBURN	2 35
1 11	NEWPORT PAGNELL	1 44 a.m.
4 23	MARKET HARBOROUGH	10 32
5 54	LEICESTER	9 07
6 50	LOUGHBOROUGH	8 05
8 17	NOTTINGHAM	6 08
11 17	CHESTERFIELD	3 33
12 30 p.m.	SHEFFIELD	2 13 p.m.
3 18	HUDDERSFIELD	11 32
4 05	HALIFAX	10 45 a.m.

LONDON & LEEDS — ROYAL MAIL
E. Sherman & Co.

7 30 p.m.	LONDON Bull & Mouth, St. Martin's-le-Grand	6 29
8 00	LONDON General Post Office	6 14
9 11	BARNET	5 03
10 39	WELWYN	3 40
11 34	HITCHIN	2 44
1 14 a.m.	BEDFORD	12 52 p.m.
2 46	HIGHAM FERRERS	11 20
3 46	KETTERING	10 20
5 16	UPPINGHAM	8 50
5 55	OAKHAM	8 11
6 57	MELTON MOWBRAY	6 44
9 11	NOTTINGHAM	4 37
10 45	MANSFIELD	3 13
12 03 p.m.	CHESTERFIELD	1 52
1 19	SHEFFIELD	12 26 a.m.
2 55	BARNSLEY	11 05
3 58	WAKEFIELD	10 02
4 52	LEEDS	9 08 p.m.

LONDON & GLASGOW   ROYAL MAIL
E. Sherman & Co.

7 30 p.m.	LONDON Bull & Mouth, St. Martin's – le – Grand	5 28
8 00	LONDON General Post Office	5 13
9 18	BARNET	3 55
10 46	WELWYN	2 24
12 06 a.m.	BALDOCK	1 04 a.m
3 56	STILTON	9 08
5 28	STAMFORD	7 33
7 40	GRANTHAM	5 06
9 44	NEWARK	2 54
11 03	OLLERTON	1 35
11 52	WORKSOP	12 46 p.m.
1 26 p.m.	DONCASTER	11 12
2 53	PONTEFRACT	9 45
4 16	WETHERBY	7 22
5 48	BOROUGHBRIDGE	6 10
10 02	GRETA BRIDGE	2 30
12 15 a.m.	BROUGH	12 14 a.m.
1 07	APPLEBY	11 18
2 28	PENRITH	9 53
4 17	CARLISLE	8 00
5 55	GRETNA	4 54
6 48	ECCLEFECHAN	4 01 p.m.
11 18	DOUGLAS MILL	10 51
12 57 p.m.	HAMILTON	9 02
2 00	GLASGOW	7 55 a.m.

LONDON – EDINBURGH – THURSO   ROYAL MAIL
E. Sherman & Co.

7 30 p.m.	LONDON Bull & Mouth, St. Martin's-le-Grand	5 52
8 00	LONDON General Post Office	5 37
9 25	WALTHAM CROSS	4 12
10 26	WARE	3 10
12 57 a.m.	ARRINGTON	12 33 a.m.
2 30	HUNTINGDON	10 53
3 45	STILTON	9 33
5 15	STAMFORD	7 45
7 23	GRANTHAM	4 45
9 30	NEWARK	3 16
11 49	BARNBY MOOR	12 50 p.m.
1 12 p.m.	DONCASTER	11 12
2 44	FERRYBRIDGE	9 36
3 56	TADCASTER	8 16
4 54	YORK	6 31
6 54	EASINGWOLD	5 07
7 58	THIRSK	3 59
8 52	NORTHALLERTON	3 01
10 28	DARLINGTON	1 17 a.m.
12 33 a.m.	DURHAM	11 12
1 50	NEWCASTLE UPON TYNE	9 22
3 22	MORPETH	7 47
5 17	ALNWICK	5 41
6 47	BELFORD	3 36
8 17	BERWICK-UPON-TWEED	2 01 p.m.
11 41	DUNBAR	10 55
12 45 p.m.	HADDINGTON	9 46
2 23	EDINBURGH	8 00 a.m.
4 00 p.m.	EDINBURGH	6 00
7 15	KINROSS	2 47
9 00	PERTH	12 52 p.m.
11 15	DUNDEE	10 32
1 06 a.m.	ARBROATH	8 27
2 23	MONTROSE	7 03
4 47	STONEHAVEN	4 37
6 22	ABERDEEN	3 00 a.m.

SERVICE NORTH OF ABERDEEN ON OPPOSITE PAGE

LONDON – EDINBURGH – THURSO   ROYAL MAIL
E. Sherman & Co.

SERVICE SOUTH OF ABERDEEN ON OPPOSITE PAGE

6 22	ABERDEEN	12 15 a.m.
8 54	INVERURIE	10 44
11 45	HUNTLY	7 23
12 58 p.m.	KEITH	6 10
3 00	ELGIN	4 03
6 02	NAIRN	1 13 p.m.
8 06	INVERNESS	11 00
12 30 a.m.	BEAULY	7 05
1 30	DINGWALL	6 05
4 30	TAIN	2 45
6 40	DORNOCH	12 55 a.m.
8 20	GOLSPIE	10 45
11 15	HELMSDALE	8 20
3 20 p.m.	LYBSTER	3 50
5 10	WICK	2 00 p.m.
8 10	THURSO	11 00 a.m.

LONDON & BARTON-UPON-HUMBER (for HULL) ROYAL MAIL
W. Chaplin & Co.

7 30 p.m.	LONDON Spread Eagle, Gracechurch Street	6 40
8 00	LONDON General Post Office	6 25
9 25	WALTHAM CROSS	5 00
12 16 a.m.	BALDOCK	2 09 a.m.
4 46	PETERBOROUGH	9 24
6 22	BOURNE	7 48
7 16	FOLKINGHAM	6 54
8 08	SLEAFORD	5 57
10 22	LINCOLN	3 43
12 54 p.m.	BRIGG	1 21
2 00	BARTON-UPON-HUMBER Waterside	12 15 p.m.

LONDON & LOUTH   ROYAL MAIL
R. Fagg & Co.

7 30 p.m.	LONDON Bell & Crown, Holborn	6 26 ↑
8 00	LONDON General Post Office	6 11
9 25	WALTHAM CROSS	4 46
10 30 ↓	WARE	3 45
12 53 a.m.	ARRINGTON	1 18
1 32	CAXTON	12 39 a.m.
2 26	HUNTINGDON	11 45 ↑
4 24	PETERBOROUGH	9 32
6 34	SPALDING	7 27
8 09	BOSTON	5 37
10 15	SPILSBY	3 56
11 56 ↓	LOUTH	2 15 p.m.

LONDON – LYNN – WELLS   ROYAL MAIL
W. Chaplin & Co. / R. Fagg & Co.

7 30 p.m.	LONDON Swan with Two Necks, Lad Lane (A)	6 23 ↑
7 30 p.m.	LONDON Bell & Crown, Holborn (A)	6 23
8 00	LONDON General Post Office	6 08
10 32 ↓	WADESMILL	3 36
12 31 a.m.	MELBOURNE	1 37
1 36	CAMBRIDGE	12 02 a.m.
3 31	ELY	10 22 ↑
5 21	DOWNHAM	8 32
6 33 ↓	LYNN	7 20 p.m.

7 00 a.m.	LYNN	6 50 ↑
8 13	SNETTISHAM	5 35
10 05	BURNHAM MARKET	3 43
10 43 ↓	WELLS	3 05 p.m.

A - Terminates alternately.

LONDON & NORWICH — ROYAL MAIL
R. Nelson & Co.

7 30 p.m.	LONDON Belle Sauvage, Ludgate Hill	6 44
8 00	LONDON General Post Office	6 29
11 30	BISHOPS STORTFORD	2 59
12 52 a.m.	LITTLEBURY	1 31 a.m.
2 54	NEWMARKET	11 21
4 27	BURY ST. EDMUNDS	9 33
5 52	THETFORD	8 13
7 27	ATTLEBOROUGH	6 38
9 05	NORWICH	5 00 p.m.

LONDON & NORWICH — ROYAL MAIL
W. Chaplin & Co.

7 30 p.m.	LONDON Spread Eagle, Gracechurch Street	6 58
8 00	LONDON General Post Office	6 43
10 30	INGATESTONE	4 13
11 57	WITHAM	2 46
1 23 a.m.	COLCHESTER	1 20 a.m.
3 12	IPSWICH	11 21
5 09	STOKE	9 32
6 37	LONG STRATTON	8 01
7 38	NORWICH	7 00 p.m.

LONDON & YARMOUTH — ROYAL MAIL
W. Chaplin & Co.

7 30 p.m.	LONDON White Horse, Fetter Lane	6 58
8 00	LONDON General Post Office	6 43
10 30	INGATESTONE	4 13
11 57	WITHAM	2 46
1 23 a.m.	COLCHESTER	1 20 a.m.
3 12	IPSWICH	11 21
4 47	WICKHAM MARKET	9 41
6 15	YOXFORD	8 23
9 30	YARMOUTH	5 00 p.m.

TABLE 2A
CROSS-COUNTRY & LOCAL
ROYAL MAIL COACHES

	DEPARTURE TIME	
	OUTWARD	RETURN
ABERDEEN & BALLATER	7 00 a.m.	8 00 a.m.
ABERDEEN & PETERHEAD	8 00 a.m.	9 00 a.m.
ABERGAVENNY & MERTHYR	1 15 p.m.	9 30 a.m.
BANGOR & PWLLHELI	7 00 a.m.	3 00 p.m.
BARNSTAPLE & ILFRACOMBE	6 08 p.m.	6 00 a.m.
BIRMINGHAM & LEAMINGTON	8 00 a.m.	3 00 p.m.
BIRMINGHAM & LIVERPOOL	7 00 a.m.	7 00 p.m.
BIRMINGHAM & SHEFFIELD	5 30 a.m.	8 00 a.m.
BIRMINGHAM & STOURPORT	8 00 a.m.	3 15 p.m.
BIRMINGHAM & STRATFORD UPON AVON	7 15 a.m.	3 00 p.m.
BIRMINGHAM & WALSALL	8 00 a.m.	11 00 a.m.
	3 00 p.m.	5 00 p.m.
BIRMINGHAM & WORCESTER	7 45 a.m.	3 00 p.m.
BIRMINGHAM & YARMOUTH	7 45 a.m.	4 30 p.m.
BRIDPORT & TAUNTON	6 20 a.m.	4 12 p.m.
BRISTOL & BATH	6 45 a.m.	4 30 p.m.
	9 15 a.m.	3 00 p.m.
BRISTOL & BIDEFORD	8 10 a.m.	7 03 a.m.
BRISTOL & LIVERPOOL	7 05 p.m.	5 05 p.m.
BRISTOL & MANCHESTER	8 00 p.m.	9 15 a.m.
BRISTOL & PORTSMOUTH	7 00 p.m.	7 00 p.m.
CAMBRIDGE & HOLBEACH	2 00 a.m.	4 30 p.m.
CANTERBURY & DEAL	4 00 a.m.	6 30 p.m.
CARDIFF & MERTHYR	3 00 p.m.	7 00 a.m.
CHALFORD & WOTTON UNDER EDGE	8 00 a.m.	5 15 p.m.
CHELTENHAM & ABERYSTWYTH	7 20 a.m.	5 45 a.m.
CHELTENHAM & BATH	7 00 a.m.	2 30 p.m.
COLDBLOW & HAVERFORDWEST	11 00 p.m.	1 15 a.m.
DERBY & MANCHESTER	9 30 a.m.	9 00 a.m.
DEVIZES & WELLS	5 50 a.m.	4 45 p.m.

DEVONPORT & LAUNCESTON	5 24 p.m.	5 30 a.m.
DONCASTER & YORK	1 45 p.m.	6 15 a.m.
EDINBURGH & CARLISLE	7 00 a.m.	5 20 a.m.
EDINBURGH & DUMFRIES	9 30 p.m.	6 30 a.m.
EDINBURGH & GLASGOW	9 30 p.m.	10 30 p.m.
	12 10 p.m.	12 35 p.m.
EDINBURGH & STIRLING	4 00 p.m.	8 30 a.m.
EXETER & BUDLEIGH SALTERTON	4 00 p.m.	7 00 a.m.
EXETER & DARTMOUTH	1 15 p.m.	7 30 a.m.
FRASERBURGH & BURNESS	7 40 a.m.	10 45 p.m.
GLASGOW & PERTH	1 00 p.m.	1 09 a.m.
GLASGOW & PORT PATRICK	5 00 p.m.	3 00 p.m.
GLOUCESTER & BRIGHTON	1 35 a.m.	7 30 a.m.
GRANTHAM & NOTTINGHAM	8 00 a.m.	1 30 p.m.
KINGSBRIDGE & ASHBURTON	8 55 a.m.	3 00 p.m.
LANCASTER & CLAPHAM	7 00 a.m.	5 00 p.m.
LEEDS & HALIFAX	5 20 p.m.	5 45 a.m.
LEEDS & PONTEFRACT	2 53 p.m.	8 00 a.m.
LEICESTER & BURTON UPON TRENT	6 30 a.m.	3 00 p.m.
LEOMINSTER & PRESTEIGNE	1 00 p.m.	10 00 a.m.
LIVERPOOL & HOLYHEAD	6 00 p.m.	4 45 p.m.
LIVERPOOL & LANCASTER	8 15 a.m.	11 30 a.m.
LIVERPOOL & MANCHESTER by Railway	10 00 a.m.	7 00 a.m.
	12 00 noon	10 00 a.m.
	2 00 p.m.	2 00 p.m.
	5 00 p.m.	5 00 p.m.
LIVERPOOL & PRESTON	4 30 p.m.	4 15 a.m.
LOUTH & GRIMSBY	12 30 p.m.	10 00 a.m.
LOUTH & SHEFFIELD	5 15 a.m.	8 45 a.m.
MANCHESTER & BLACKBURN	4 00 p.m.	5 00 a.m.
MANCHESTER & COLNE	4 00 p.m.	4 15 a.m.
MANCHESTER & GLOSSOP	4 00 p.m.	6 00 a.m.
MANCHESTER & KNUTSFORD	8 00 p.m.	4 15 a.m.
MANCHESTER & STALYBRIDGE	7 00 a.m.	1 30 p.m.
MANCHESTER & YORK	8 30 a.m.	7 00 a.m.
	8 00 p.m.	9 00 p.m.
NEWPORT (Mon.) & ABERGAVENNY	1 45 a.m.	8 00 a.m.
NEWTON STEWART & STRANRAER	4 00 p.m.	6 00 a.m.
NORWICH & CROMER	9 30 a.m.	1 40 p.m.
NORWICH & YARMOUTH	9 30 a.m.	1 45 p.m.
PERTH & INVERNESS	9 00 p.m.	9 00 a.m.

PETERHEAD & BANFF	8 30 a.m.	3 30 p.m.
PONTEFRACT & LEEDS	2 55 p.m.	8 00 a.m.
ROCHDALE & BOLTON	6 00 a.m.	5 00 p.m.
SALISBURY & CHRISTCHURCH	5 30 a.m.	5 30 p.m.
SALISBURY & EXETER	4 52 a.m.	12 00 p.m.
SHREWSBURY & BIRMINGHAM	7 00 a.m.	2 00 p.m.
SHREWSBURY & NEWTOWN	1 00 p.m.	8 00 a.m.
SOUTHAMPTON & LYMINGTON	6 15 a.m.	5 30 p.m.
SWANSEA & MERTHYR	7 00 a.m.	2 00 p.m.
TAMWORTH & BIRMINGHAM	7 40 a.m.	4 00 p.m.
TAUNTON & MINEHEAD	2 15 p.m.	7 45 a.m.
TAUNTON & SIDMOUTH	2 00 p.m.	8 15 a.m.
WORCESTER & KINGTON	8 50 a.m.	12 47 a.m.
YORK & HULL	7 00 a.m.	4 00 p.m.
	7 30 p.m.	11 00 a.m.
YORK & SCARBOROUGH	7 00 a.m.	3 00 p.m.

TABLE 3

CROSS – COUNTRY

AND

LOCAL STAGE COACHES OUTSIDE LONDON

SERVICE MILES	PROPRIETOR	COACHES	FREQUENCY
ABERGAVENNY & MERTHYR			
20	E. Pinchase & Co.	7745 (4-4)	1 ret. jny. daily
ABERGAVENNY & MONMOUTH CAP			
12	J. Barnett	7647 (9—)	1 ret. jny. Tues. only
ABERGAVENNY & NEWPORT Mon.			
22½	E. Lewis & Co.	7700 (4-5)	1 ret. jny. daily
ABERGAVENNY & ROSS			
26	T. Heath & Co.	7637 (4-5)	1 ret. jny. Mon. to Sat.
ABERGELE & VORYD			
4	J. Hughes	8347 (15—)	1 ret. jny. Mon. to Fri.
ABINGDON & DORCHESTER Oxon.			
6	R. Costar & Co.	7211 (4-5)	1 ret. jny. Mon. to Sat.
AIGBURTH & CROSBY			
11	J. Newton	9453 (8-4)	1 ret. jny. Mon. to Sat.
AINTREE & CROSBY VILLAGE			
12	S. Towers	9466 (12-6)	1 ret. jny. Sat. only
AINTREE & KNOTTY ASH			
10	M. Dickenson	9471 (8-4)	1 ret. jny. Mon. only
AINTREE & OLD SWAN			
8½	J. Bunnell	9472 (8-4)	1 ret. jny. Mon. only
AINTREE & PRESCOT			
12½	J. Holden	9417 (4-8)	1 ret. jny. Mon. only
AINTREE & WOOLTON			
10	J. Newton	9434 (8-4)	1 ret. jny. Mon. only
ALCESTER & STRATFORD-UPON-AVON			
8	T. Butler	7584 (4-5)	1 ret. jny. Fri. only
ALDRIDGE & WOLVERHAMPTON			
10	W. Tookey	8070 (6-3)	1 ret. jny. Wed. only
AMERSHAM & RICKMANSWORTH			
8	W. Wyatt & Co.	10011 (2-4)	1 ret. jny. Mon. to Sat.
AMERSHAM ROAD (Rose & Crown) & UXBRIDGE			
9	W. Tollitt	10008 (2-4)	1 ret. jny. Mon. to Sat.
ASHFORD & FAVERSHAM			
12	W. Bills	6305 (4—)	1 ret. jny. Tu., Th., Sat.
ASHFORD & LYDD			
17	W. Blacklocks	6308 (4—)	1 ret. jny. Mon. to Sat.
AXMINSTER & LYME REGIS			
5	W. Stephens & Co.	5528 (2-2)	1 ret. jny. Mon. to Sat.

BANGOR & CAERNARVON

9	H. Bicknell	8348 (4-8)	I ret. jny. Mon. to Sat.
9	G. Evans	8351 (4-5)	I ret. jny. Mon. to Sat.
9	R. Rowland	8352 (4-5)	I ret. jny. Mon. to Sat.

BANGOR & HOLYHEAD

25	R. Spencer & Co.	8356 (4-8)	I ret. jny. daily

BANGOR & PWLLHELI

29	H. Bicknell & Co.	8349 (4-5)	I ret. jny. daily

BARMOUTH & DRUID INN

38	W. Barnett & Co.	8350 (4-8)	I ret. jny. Tu., Th., Sat.

BARNSLEY & ROTHERHAM

11	R. Marshall	8633 (6 —)	I ret. jny. Wed. only

BARNSTAPLE & DEVONPORT

64	W. Elliott & Co.	5635 (4-8)	I sgl. jny. Mon. to Sat.

BATH & BATHFORD

3	D. Davies	5828 (5-4)	2 ret. jnys. Mon. to Sat.

BATH & BRADFORD-ON-AVON

8	J. Wheeler	6015 (4-2)	I ret. jny. Mon. to Sat.

BATH & CHELTENHAM

50	M. Pickwick & Co.	5855, 5857 (4-8)	I ret. jny. Mon. to Sat.

BATH & CHIPPENHAM

13	W. Lawes & Co.	6006 (4-8)	I ret. jny. Mon. to Sat.
13	W. Deadman & Co.	6008 (4-8)	I ret. jny. Mon., Wed., Sat.

BATH & CLIFTON

15	J. Burt & Co.	7443 (4-5)	I ret. jny. Mon. to Sat.
15	C. Smith	5836 (4-5)	I ret. jny. daily
15	W. Lane	5825 (4-5)	I ret. jny. Mon. to Sat.
15	R. Coward	5826 (4-8)	I ret. jny. Mon. to Sat.
15	M. Pickwick	5827 (4-8)	I ret. jny. Mon. to Sat.

BATH & TROWBRIDGE

11	J. Lucas	6007 (4-5)	I ret. jny. Mon., Tu., Wed., Fri., Sat.

BATH & EXETER

81	J. Cockram & Co.	5563 (4-8)	I sgl. jny. Mon. to Sat.
81	M. Pickwick & Co.	5856 (4-8)	I sgl. jny. Mon. to Sat.
82	W. Stephens & Co.	5586, 5589 (4-8)	I ret. jny. Mon. to Sat.

BATH & LYME

65	C. Smith & Co.	5821 (4-5)	I sgl. jny. Mon. to Sat.

BATH & POOLE

62	M. Pickwick & Co.	5971 (4-8)	I sgl. jny. Mon. to Sat.

BATH & READING

69	W. Lane & Co.	5842, 5843 (4-5)	I ret. jny. Mon. to Sat.

BATH & SHREWSBURY

| 120 | W. Lane & Co. | 5834 (4-8) | I sgl. jny. Mon. to Sat. |

BATH & SIDMOUTH

| 74 | W. Lane & Co. | 5839 (4-5) | I sgl. jny. Mon. to Sat. |

BATH & SOUTHAMPTON

| 62 | M. Pickwick & Co. | 5851 (4-8) | I sgl. jny. Mon. to Sat. |
| 62 | W. Lane & Co. | 5841 (4-8) | I sgl. jny. Mon. to Sat. |

BATH & TAUNTON

| 52 | J. Martin & Co. | 5832 (4-8) | I sgl. jny. Mon. to Sat. |

BATH & WARMINSTER

| 17 | T. Rodaway | 6003 (4-5) | I ret. jny. Mon. to Sat. |

BATH & WESTBURY

| 15 | M. Genish & Co. | 6001 (4-8) | I ret. jny. Mon. to Sat. |

BATH & WEYMOUTH

| 65 | M. Pickwick & Co. | 5852 (4-8) | I sgl. jny. Mon. to Sat. |
| 65 | W. Lane & Co. | 5847 (4-8) | I sgl. jny. Mon. to Sat. |

BECCLES & WANGFORD

| 8 | D. Hogarth & Co. | 6706 (4-2) | I ret. jny. daily |

BEDFORD & WOBURN

| 15 | D. Whiteman | 6861 (4-2) | I ret. jny. Sat. only |

BERWICK & ALNWICK

| 29 | J. Burn & Co. | 9974 (4-8) | I ret. jny. daily |

BERWICK & KELSO

| 73 | C. Mitchell & Co. | 9841 (4-8) | I ret. jny. Tu. & Fri. |

BERWICK & WOOLER

| 17 | W. Fairnington | 9977 (4-8) | I ret. jny. Sat. only |

BIRKENHEAD & PARKGATE

| 9 | J. Bloor | 8249 (4-8) | I ret. jny. Mon. to Sat. |

BIRMINGHAM & ALCESTER

| 19 | T. Butler | 7584 (4-5) | I ret. jny. Th. only |
| 20 | J. Clarke | 7058 (4-8) | I ret. jny. Th. only |

BIRMINGHAM & ALDRIDGE

| 9 | W. Tookey | 8070 (6-3) | I ret. jny. Th. only |

BIRMINGHAM & ATHERSTONE

| 20 | H. Smith | 7066 (4-8) | I ret. jny. Mon., Th., Sat. |

BIRMINGHAM & BATH

92	M. Pickwick & Co.	5853 (4-8)	I sgl. jny. Mon. to Sat.
94	W. Lane & Co.	5846 (4-8)	I sgl. jny. Mon. to Sat.
90	C. Stovin & Co.	7015 (4-8)	I sgl. jny. Mon. to Sat.
94	N. Vyse & Co.	7027 (4-8)	I sgl. jny. Mon. to Sat.

BIRMINGHAM & BEWDLEY
20   J. Barnett   7524 (9 —)   1 ret. jny. Mon./Tu., Th./Fri.

BIRMINGHAM & BIRKENHEAD
91   Radenhurst & Co. 8229,8230 (4-11) 1 ret. jny. daily

BIRMINGHAM & BLOXWICH
10   G. Stokes   7073 (4-8) 1 ret. jny. Tu., Th., Sat.

BIRMINGHAM & BRISTOL
93   J. Townsend & Co. 5696 (4-8) 1 sgl. jny. Mon. to Sat.
87   J. Townsend & Co. 5698 (4-8) 1 sgl. jny. Tu. to Sun.
94   T. Waddell & Co. 7021 (4-8) 1 sgl. jny. Mon. to Sat.
87   T. Chapman & Co. 7025 (4-8) 1 sgl. jny. Tu. to Sun.

BIRMINGHAM & BROMSGROVE
13   J. Blower   7514 (8-4) 1 ret. jny. Mon. & Th.
13   T. Albut   7516 (8-1) 1 ret. jny. Mon. & Th.

BIRMINGHAM & BURSLEM
47   W. Maison & Co. 8099 (4-8) 1 ret. jny. Mon. to Sat.

BIRMINGHAM & CAMBRIDGE
100   M. Copps & Co. 6919 (4-5) 1 sgl. jny. Mon. to Sat.

BIRMINGHAM & CHELTENHAM
50   J. Nayler & Co. 7391 (4-5) 1 sgl. jny. Mon. to Sat.
50   J. Nayler & Co. 7386 (4-8) 1 sgl. jny. Mon. to Sat.
50   T. Haines & Co. 7576 (4-5) 1 sgl. jny. Mon. to Sat.
49   W. Waddell & Co. 7020 (4-8) 1 sgl. jny. Mon. to Sat.

BIRMINGHAM & COLESHILL
10   C. Farr & Co. 7107 (9-3) 1 ret. jny. Mon., Th., Sat.
10   W. Brookes 7115 (4 —) 1 ret. jny. Th. only

BIRMINGHAM & COVENTRY
18   T. Chapman & Co. 7037 (4-8) 1 ret. jny. Mon. to Sat.

BIRMINGHAM & DERBY
42   T. Waddell & Co. 7038 (4-8) 1 ret. jny. Mon. to Sat.
42   T. Chapman & Co. 7113 (4-11) 1 ret. jny. Mon. to Sat.

BIRMINGHAM & DUDLEY
10   J. Doughty 7013 (14-1) 3 ret. jnys. daily
10   T. Chapman & Co. 7024 (4-11) 2 ret. jnys. Mon. to Sat.
9   T. Eves 7052 (4-11) 1 ret. jny. daily
10   J. Hughes 7056 (12-6) 2 ret. jnys. daily
9   W. Eves & Co. 7061 (4-11) 1 ret. jny. daily

BIRMINGHAM & EASTHAM FERRY
82   R. Smith & Co. 8236 (4-11) 1 sgl. jny. daily
81   T. Icke 7017 (4-11) 1 sgl. jny. daily

BIRMINGHAM & EDGBASTON

2	J. Smith	7116 (11-1)	7 ret. jnys. Mon. to Sat., 5 ret. jnys. Sun.
2	J. Doughty	7119 (11-1)	6 ret. jnys. daily

BIRMINGHAM & GLOUCESTER

55	T. Chapman & Co.	7028, 7077 (4-8)	1 ret. jny. Mon. to Sat.

BIRMINGHAM & HANLEY

45	T. Lea & Co.	8095 (4-8)	1 ret. jny. daily

BIRMINGHAM & HENLEY IN ARDEN

14	W. Johns & Co.	7069 (4-11)	1 ret. jny. Mon. & Th.

BIRMINGHAM & KIDDERMINSTER

18	T. Fawkner	7525 (10-2)	1 ret. jny. Tu./Wed., Fri./Sat.
21¼	H. Godfrey & Co.	7512 (4-8)	1 sgl. jny. daily
21½	C. Radenhurst & Co.	7528 (4-8)	1 sgl. jny. daily

BIRMINGHAM & LEAMINGTON

22	T. Chapman & Co.	7031, 7032, 7033 (4-8)	3 ret. jnys. Mon. to Sat.
22	T. Pugh	7047, 7048 (4-8)	2 ret. jnys. daily

BIRMINGHAM & LEEDS

109	M. Outhwaite & Co.	8416 (4-11)	1 sgl. jny. Mon. to Sat.
105	C. Stovin & Co.	7014 (4-11)	1 sgl. jny. Mon. to Sat.

BIRMINGHAM & LEICESTER

44	J. G. Briggs & Co.	6966 (4-11)	1 sgl. jny. Mon. to Sat.
44	C. Stovin & Co.	7016 (4-11)	1 sgl. jny. Mon. to Sat.
44	C. S. Pettifor & Co.	6957 (4-8)	1 sgl. jny. Mon. to Sat.
44	C. S. Pettifor & Co.	6964 (4-11)	1 ret. jny. Mon. to Sat.
44	C. Radenhurst & Co.	7083 (4-11)	1 sgl. jny. Mon. to Sat.

BIRMINGHAM & LICHFIELD

15	T. Chapman & Co.	7044 (4-11)	1 ret. jny. Mon. to Sat.

BIRMINGHAM & NORTHAMPTON

48	T. Chapman & Co.	7041 (4-8)	1 ret. jny. Mon., Wed., Fri.

BIRMINGHAM & NOTTINGHAM

50	J. Simpson & Co.	7894, 7920 (4-11)	1 ret. jny. Mon. to Sat.

BIRMINGHAM & NUNEATON

22	J. Bell	7080 (6 —)	1 ret. jny. Mon., Th., Sat.

BIRMINGHAM & OXFORD

61	R. Costar & Co.	7202, 7203 (4-8)	1 ret. jny. Mon. to Sat.
60½	T. Penin & Co.	7240, 7241 (4-5)	1 ret. jny. Mon. to Sat.

BIRMINGHAM & REDDITCH

14	T. Chapman & Co.	7515 (4-8)	1 ret. jny. daily

BIRMINGHAM & RUGELEY

22	J. Wolfinden	7046 (4-11)	1 ret. jny. Mon. to Sat.

BIRMINGHAM & SHEFFIELD

77	W.L. Bickley & Co.	7074 (4-11)	1 sgl. jny. Mon. to Sat.
77	W.L. Bickley & Co.	8646 (4-8)	1 sgl. jny. Mon. to Sat.
84	W.L. Bickley & Co.	8650 (4-11)	1 sgl. jny. Mon. to Sat.
84	T. Chapman & Co.	7078 (4-11)	1 sgl. jny. Mon. to Sat.

BIRMINGHAM & SHREWSBURY

43	J. Jobson & Co.	8145, 8146 (4-5)	1 ret. jny. daily
44	T. Waddell & Co.	7019, 7035 (4-11)	1 ret. jny. daily
45	W. Hemming & Co.	7029, 7055 (4-11)	1 ret. jny. daily

BIRMINGHAM & SOLIHULL

| 7 | J. Fairfield | 7051 (8-4) | 1 ret. jny. Mon., Th., Sat. |

BIRMINGHAM & STOURBRIDGE

12	J. Simpson	7519 (4-11)	1 ret. jny. daily ex. Fri.
13	J. Simpson	7530 (4-5)	1 ret. jny. Mon., Th., Fri., Sat.
12	J. Simpson	7531 (4-8)	1 ret. jny. daily
15	C. Harrold & Co.	7011 (4-8)	1 ret. jny. daily
12	C.O. Gray	7101 (4-8)	1 ret. jny. Wed., Fri., Sun.

BIRMINGHAM & SUTTON COLDFIELD

| 7 | C. Smith | 7059 (4-11) | 1 ret. jny. Tu., Wed., Fri., 2 ret. jnys. Mon., Th., Sat. |

BIRMINGHAM & TAMWORTH

| 15 | J. Clarke & Co. | 7108 (4-5) | 1 ret. jny. Tu., Th., Sat. |
| 15 | J. Riley | 7049 (15 —) | 1 ret. jny. Tu., Th., Sat. |

BIRMINGHAM & WALSALL

8	R.M. Fletcher & Co.	8075 (4-11)	2 ret. jnys. Mon. to Sat.
8	J. Shorters	8081 (12-6)	1 ret. jny. daily
8	T. Chapman & Co.	7117 (4-5)	2 ret. jnys. daily
8	R. Middlemore	8098 (4-11)	2 ret. jnys. Mon., Tu., Fri., Sat., 1 ret. jny. Sun.

BIRMINGHAM & WARWICK

| 20 | T. Chapman & Co. | 7079 (4-11) | 1 ret. jny. Tu., Th. |

BIRMINGHAM & WEDNESBURY

| 8 | J. Collier | 8082 (4-11) | 1 ret. jny. Mon., Tu., Th., Sat., Sun. |
| 8 | C. Cross | 7050 (10-5) | 1 ret. jny. Mon. to Sat. |

BIRMINGHAM & WEST BROMWICH

6	J. Doughty	7071 (14-1)	6 ret. jnys. daily
6	J. Doughty	7109 (12-3)	1 ret. jny. Mon. & Sat.
6	J. Doughty	7111 (14-1)	2 ret. jnys. Mon., 1 ret. jny. Tu.

BIRMINGHAM & WOODSIDE

| 89 | J. Poole & Co. | 8206 (4-11) | 1 sgl. jny. Mon. to Sat. |
| 90 | N. Vyse & Co. | 7043 (4-4) | 1 sgl. jny. Mon. to Sat. |

BIRMINGHAM & WOLVERHAMPTON

13	T. Brookes & Co.	7053 (4-8)	1 ret. jny. daily
13	T. Brookes & Co.	7054 (4-11)	1 ret. jny. daily ex. Wed.
13	T. Smith	7099 (4-11)	1 ret. jny. Mon. to Sat.
13	J. A. Best	7105 (4-8)	1 sgl. jny. daily
13	J. Horton	7106 (4-8)	1 sgl. jny. daily

BIRMINGHAM & WORCESTER

26	J. Jones & Co.	7570 (4-8)	1 ret. jny. Mon. to Sat.
26	T. Reeves & Co.	7577 (4-8)	1 ret. jny. Mon. to Sat.

BIRMINGHAM & YARMOUTH

199½	D. Hogarth & Co.	6736, 6737 (4-8)	1 sgl. jny. daily
199	T. Waddell & Co.	7063, 7064 (4-8)	1 sgl. jny. daily

BLACKBURN & BLACKPOOL

30	W. Frankland & Co.	9405 (8-4)	1 ret. jny. Th.
32	J. Croft & Co.	8966 (4-8)	1 ret. jny. daily

BLACKBURN & BOLTON

12½	J. Briggs	9446 (4—)	1 ret. jny. Mon. only

BLACKBURN & CLITHEROE

10	R. Smalley	9439 (6—)	1 ret. jny. Wed. only
10	M. Standen	9442 (8-4)	1 ret. jny. Wed. only

BLACKBURN & GISBURN

18	W. Frankland & Co.	9405 (8-4)	1 ret. jny. alt. Mon.

BLACKBURN & SKIPTON

20	W. Frankland & Co.	9405 (8-4)	1 ret. jny. alt. Mon.

BLACKMORE & BRENTWOOD

7	J. Murrells	10001 (4-2)	1 ret. jny. Mon. & Sat., 1 sgl. jny. Tu. to Fri.

BODMIN & TORPOINT

30	W. Rowe	5504 (6—)	1 sgl. jny. Mon. to Sat.

BOGNOR & LITTLEHAMPTON

14	B. W. Horne & Co.	6173 (4-5)	1 sgl. jny. daily

BOLTON & CHORLEY

11	H. Shalden	9093 (—6)	1 ret. jny. Mon., Wed., Th., Fri., Sat.

BOLTON & HEYWOOD

8	G. Massey & Co.	9061 (6-9)	1 ret. jny. Mon. only

BOSTON & NEW HOLLAND

64	D. Jackson & Co.	7834, 7843 (4-8)	1 ret. jny. Mon. to Sat.

BOSTON & STAMFORD

35	D. Jackson & Co.	7821 (4-5)	1 ret. jny. Mon. to Sat.

BRACKLEY & BARLEY MOW

2	J. Hearn & Co.	10031 (3-3)	1 sgl. jny. Mon. to Sat.

BRADFORD & DEWSBURY			
9	T. Wormald	8826 (4-11)	I ret. jny. Th. only
BRADFORD & HUDDERSFIELD			
11	J. Hirst	8807 (4-11)	I ret. jny. Tu. only
BRADFORD & KEIGHLEY			
10	J. Walker	8435 (4-8)	I ret. jny. Th. only
BRADFORD & SKIPTON			
20	J. Frances & Co.	8813 (4-8)	I ret. jny. Mon. to Sat.
BRADFORD & WAKEFIELD			
14	T. Dunmill	8799 (4-5)	I ret. jny. Th. only
14	T. Bradford & Co.	8792 (4-5)	I ret. jny. Mon. to Sat.
BRADFORD-ON-AVON & MELKSHAM			
7½	S. Mountain & Co.	6013 (4 —)	I sgl. jny. Mon. & Sun., I ret. jny. Tu. to Sat.
BRAINTREE & HALSTEAD			
7	S. Hayward	6597 (4-5)	I ret. jny. Mon. to Sat.
BRECON & BRIMFIELD			
43	W. Jones & Co.	7777 (4-5)	I sgl. jny. Mon. to Sat.
BRECON & MERTHYR TYDFIL			
18	J. Edwards	7773 (4-5)	I sgl. jny. Mon. to Sat.
BRECON & TENBY			
72	W. Jones & Co.	7771 (4-8)	I sgl. jny. Mon. to Sat.
BREWOOD & WOLVERHAMPTON			
7	J. Hay	8093 (4-8)	I ret. jny. Wed. only
BRIDGNORTH & STOURBRIDGE			
14½	T. Gough	7511 (4 —)	I ret. jny. Sat. only
BRIGHTON & CHICHESTER			
34	R. Orton & Co.	6220 (4-8)	I ret. jny. Mon. to Sat.
BRIGHTON & EASTBOURNE			
23	E. Read	6206 (4 —)	I sgl. jny. Mon. to Sat.
BRIGHTON & HASTINGS			
40	T. Crosweller & Co.	6229 (4-11)	I sgl. jny. Mon. to Sat.
40	W. Eldridge & Co.	6218 (4-8)	I sgl. jny. Mon. to Sat.
38	W. Orton	6207, 6208 (4-2)	I ret. jny. Mon. to Sat.
BRIGHTON & LEWES			
8	T. Simcock	6204 (4-2)	I ret. jny. daily
8	T. Simcock	6223 (8-4)	2 ret. jnys. daily
8	R. Baker	6205 (6 —)	I ret. jny. daily
8	T. Bryan & Co.	6222 (4-5)	I ret. jny. Mon. to Sat.
8	J. Leney	6214 (4-11)	2 ret. jnys. daily
8	J. Leney	6215 (8-1)	I ret. jny. daily

BRIGHTON & LINDFIELD
15   B. Allen   6209 (9 —) 1 ret. jny. Th. only

BRIGHTON & MAIDSTONE
51   T. Crosweller & Co. 6228 (4-8) 1 sgl. jny. Mon. to Sat.

BRIGHTON & MIDHURST
34   W. Cooper   6227 (4-5) 1 sgl. jny. Mon. to Sat.

BRIGHTON & PORTSMOUTH
48   J. Snow & Co.   6210 (4-11) 1 sgl. jny. daily
48   T. Crosweller & Co. 6203 (4-11) 1 sgl. jny. daily

BRIGHTON & READING
70   W. Stone & Co.   7224 (4-5) 1 sgl. jny. Mon. to Sat.

BRIGHTON & SHOREHAM
6   H. Hooper   6200 (4 —) 1 ret. jny. Mon. to Sat.
6   A. Cain   6201 (4 —) 1 ret. jny. Mon. to Sat.

BRIGHTON & SOUTHAMPTON
62   W. Curtis & Co. 6073, 6084 (4-8) 1 ret. jny. Mon. to Sat.

BRIGHTON & TUNBRIDGE WELLS
30   Churchill & Co. 6216 (4-8) 1 sgl. jny. Mon. to Sat.

BRIGHTON & WINDSOR
67   R. Ellis & Co.   6221 (4-8) 1 sgl. jny. Mon. to Sat.
67   T. Crosweller & Co. 6233 (4-5) 1 sgl. jny. Mon. to Sat.

BRIGHTON & WORTHING
10   J. Prescott   6213 (4-8) 1 ret. jny. daily
10   J. Snow   6226 (6-9) 1 ret. jny. daily
10   J. Snow   6234 (4-8) 1 ret. jny. daily
12   S. Toler   6175 (6 —) 1 ret. jny. Mon. to Sat.

BRILL & THAME
6   W. Taplin   10051 (2-4) 1 ret. jny. Mon., Tu., Th., Sat.

BRISTOL & BARNSTAPLE
93   J. Pearce & Co.   5521 (4-4) 1 sgl. jny. daily

BRISTOL & BATH
13   W. Clift   5707 (4-8) 1 ret. jny. daily
13   T. Hawkins & Co. 5713 (4-8) 1 ret. jny. Mon. to Sat.
13   J. Niblett & Co. 5697 (4-5) 1 ret. jny. Mon. to Sat.
13   J. Townsend & Co. 5697, 5752 (4-8) 2 ret. jnys. daily
13   T. Hawkins   5833 (4-8) 2 ret. jnys. Mon. to Sat.
13   J. K. Jones   5838 (4-5) 1 ret. jny. Mon. to Sat.
13   C. Fuller   5822 (4-5) 1 ret. jny. daily
13   J. Rose   5824 (4-8) 2 ret. jnys. Mon. to Sat.
13   J. Smith   5820 (6 —) 1 ret. jny. Mon., Wed., Fri., Sat.

BRISTOL & BRECON

55	W. Jones & Co.	7770 (4-8)	1 sgl. jny. Mon. to Sat.
55	J. Edwards & Co.	7775 (4-8)	1 sgl. jny. Mon. to Sat.

BRISTOL & BRIDGWATER

33	J. Wippell	5926 (4-8)	1 ret. jny. Mon. to Sat.

BRISTOL & BRIGHTON

135	J. Niblett & Co.	5741 (4-8)	1 sgl. jny. Mon. to Sat.

BRISTOL & CALNE

31½	J. Waller	5747 (4-5)	1 ret. jny. Mon., Th., Sat.

BRISTOL & CHALFORD

30	W. Chaplin & Co.	7380 (4-5)	1 ret. jny. Mon. to Sat.

BRISTOL & CHELTENHAM

43	J. Bland & Co.	5709 (4-8)	1 ret. jny. Mon. to Sat.
43	W. Clift & Co.	5710, 5740 (4-8)	1 ret. jny. Mon. to Sat.
43	J. Niblett & Co.	7392 (4-5)	1 ret. jny. Mon. to Sat.
43	J. Niblett & Co.	5700, 7405 (4-8)	1 ret. jny. Mon. to Sat.

BRISTOL & CLEVEDON

12	R. Leonard & Co.	5742, 5745 (4-8)	2 ret. jnys. Mon. to Sat., 1 ret. jny. Sun.
12	J. Townsend & Co.	5732 (4-8)	1 ret. jny. Mon. to Sat.

BRISTOL & DEVIZES

32	E. Parsons & Co.	6000 (4-8)	1 ret. jny. Mon. to Sat.

BRISTOL & DOWNEND

4	F. A. Dorney	7439 (6 —)	1 ret. jny. Mon., Tu., Wed., Th., Sat.

BRISTOL & DURSLEY

23	J. Hodges	7415 (4-8)	1 ret. jny. Mon., Tu., Th., Sat.

BRISTOL & EXETER

79	J. Niblett & Co.	5701 (4-8)	1 sgl. jny. daily
76	J. Niblett & Co.	5748 (4-8)	1 sgl. jny. Mon. to Sat.
76	J. Bland & Co.	5725 (4-8)	1 sgl. jny. Mon. to Sat.
76	W. Clift & Co.	5695 (4-11)	1 sgl. jny. Mon. to Sat.
79	J. Cockram & Co.	5567 (4-8)	1 sgl. jny. daily
75	W. Stephens & Co.	5580 (4-8)	1 sgl. jny. Mon. to Sat.

BRISTOL & FARRINGTON GURNEY

12	J. Niblett & Co.	5704 (4-5)	1 ret. jny. Mon. to Sat.
12	C. Smith & Co.	5721 (4-5)	1 sgl. jny. Mon. to Sat.

BRISTOL & FRAMPTON COTTEREL

7	B. Edwards	5716 (9 —)	1 ret. jny. Mon. to Sat.

BRISTOL & FROME

26	J. Wheeler	5930 (4-5)	1 ret. jny. Mon. to Sat.
26	J. Smith	5924 (6 —)	1 ret. jny. Th./Fri.

BRISTOL & HEREFORD		
52	J. Niblett & Co.	5714, 5720 (4-8) 1 ret. jny. Mon. to Sat.
BRISTOL & HOTWELLS		
2	J. Niblett & Co.	5735 (4-5) 1 ret. jny. daily
BRISTOL & KINGSWOOD HILL		
3	H.H. Budgett & Co.	5726 (9 —) 1 ret. jny. Tu., Th., Sat.
BRISTOL & MINEHEAD		
59	J. Bland & Co.	5712 (4-8) 1 sgl. jny. Mon. to Sat.
BRISTOL & OLD PASSAGE		
12	J. Richards	5737 (4-5) 1 sgl. jny. Mon. to Sat.
BRISTOL & OLVESTON		
9	J. Lippiatt	7419 (4—) 1 ret. jny. Tu., Th., Sat.
BRISTOL & PORTSMOUTH		
96	M. Pickwick & Co.	5722, 5751 (4-11) 1 ret. jny. Mon. to Sat.
BRISTOL & PUCKLECHURCH		
7	J. Raffill	5724 (4 —) 1 ret. jny. Mon., Tu., Wed., Th., Sat.
BRISTOL & SHIREHAMPTON		
5	G. Wintle	5715 (4 —) 1 ret. jny. Mon. to Sat.
BRISTOL & STROUDWATER		
30	T. Colston & Co.	7389 (4-8) 1 ret. jny. Mon. to Sat.
BRISTOL & TAUNTON		
43½	J. Niblett & Co.	5748 (4-8) 1 ret. jny. Mon. to Sat.
BRISTOL & THORNBURY		
11	J. Plowett	7418 (6 —) 1 ret. jny. Mon. to Sat.
11	T. Hendy	7381 (4-2) 1 ret. jny. Mon., Wed., Th., Sat.
BRISTOL & TROWBRIDGE		
23	M. Genish & Co.	6002 (4-5) 1 ret. jny. Mon. to Sat.
BRISTOL & WESTON-SUPER-MARE		
21	J. Harse & Co.	5711 (4-8) 1 ret. jny. Mon. to Sat.
21	W. Townsend & Co.	5705 (4-8) 1 ret. jny. Mon. to Sat.
BRISTOL & WEYMOUTH		
70	J. Niblett & Co.	5706 (4-8) 1 sgl. jny. Mon. to Sat.
68	W. Clift & Co.	5974 (4-8) 1 sgl. jny. Mon. to Sat.
BRISTOL & WRINGTON		
14	W. Shenton	5718 (4-8) 1 ret. jny. Mon., Th., Sat.
BUNGAY & IPSWICH		
37	W. Chaplin & Co.	10041 (4-2) 1 ret. jny. daily
BURLINGTON & SELBY		
45	J. Smith	8542 (4-5) 1 sgl. jny. Mon. to Sat.
BURNHAM & MALDON		
13	G. French	10016 (4-5) 1 sgl. jny. Mon. to Sat.

BURNLEY & PRESTON
22½	R. Ratcliff & Co.	9448 (4-8)	1 ret. jny. Mon. to Sat.

CAMBRIDGE & BURY ST. EDMUNDS
27	J. Deck & Co.	6664 (4-1)	1 ret. jny. Mon. to Sat.
27	J. Edwards & Co.	6666 (4-5)	1 ret. jny. Mon. to Sat.

CAMBRIDGE & COLCHESTER
48	C. Randell	6591 (4-5)	1 sgl. jny. Mon. to Sat.

CAMBRIDGE & ELY
16	W. Crabb	6833 (6—)	1 ret. jny. Mon., Wed., Sat.
16	R. Aungier	6834 (6—)	1 ret. jny. Mon., Wed., Sat.

CAMBRIDGE & HUNTINGDON
16	M. Mills	6862 (4-5)	1 ret. jny. Mon., Wed., Fri.
16	W. Ekin & Co.	6830 (4-5)	1 ret. jny. Mon. to Sat.

CAMBRIDGE & LEAMINGTON
82	T. Shaw & Co.	6918 (4-8)	1 sgl. jny. Mon., Th., Sat.
82	T. Shaw & Co.	6921 (4-8)	1 sgl. jny. Tu., Th., Sat.

CAMBRIDGE & LEICESTER
79	W. Ekin & Co.	6831 (4-11)	1 ret. jny. Mon./Tu., Wed./Th., Fri./Sat. (74 miles only on Mon., Wed., Fri.)
74	C. S. Pettifor & Co.	6971 (4-11)	1 sgl. jny. Mon. to Sat.

CAMBRIDGE & NORTHAMPTON
52	W. Ekin & Co.	6832 (4-8)	1 ret. jny. Mon., Wed., Fri.

CANTERBURY & ASHFORD
14	S. Lusted	6300 (4—)	1 ret. jny. Mon. to Sat.
14	R. Randall	6306 (4—)	1 ret. jny. Mon. to Sat.

CANTERBURY & BARHAM
6	J. Pearce	6337 (4—)	1 ret. jny. Mon., Wed., Sat.

CANTERBURY & CHARING
14	G. Down	6281 (4—)	1 ret. jny. Tu., Sat.

CANTERBURY & DEAL
18	W. B. Hook	6362 (2-7)	1 ret. jny. daily
18	W. B. Hook	6363 (2-4)	1 ret. jny. daily
18	W. B. Hook	6322 (4-5)	1 ret. jny. Mon. to Sat.
18	J. Pocket	6303 (3-1)	1 ret. jny. daily

CANTERBURY & DOVER
16	H. Worthington & Co.	6330 (4-11)	1 sgl. jny. daily
16	H. Worthington & Co.	6332 (4-5)	1 sgl. jny. Wed. & Sat.
16	H. Worthington & Co.	6329 (4-8)	1 ret. jny. daily
16	W. Clements & Co.	6341 (4-11)	1 sgl. jny. daily
16	W. Clements & Co.	6358 (4-8)	1 ret. jny. daily

(continued on next page)

CANTERBURY & DOVER— continued
16	J. Attwood	6336 (4-2) 1 ret. jny. daily
16	T. Grant	6299 (4—) 1 ret. jny. Mon. to Sat.

CANTERBURY & FAVERSHAM
9	J. Hogben	6310 (9—) 1 ret. jny. Mon. to Sat.
9	J. Hogben	6311 (9—) 1 ret. jny. Sat. only

CANTERBURY & FOLKESTONE
16	W. Ashtell	6319 (4—) 1 ret. jny. Mon., Wed., Sat.

CANTERBURY & GOODNESTONE
8	S. Hudson	6283 (4—) 1 ret. jny. Wed. & Sat.

CANTERBURY & HERNE BAY
8	W. Clements	6343 (4-2) 1 ret. jny. daily
8	W. Brown	6368 (4-2) 1 ret. jny. daily
8	E. Hopkins	6375 (2-7) 1 ret. jny. daily
8	G. Davis & Co.	6317 (2-4) 1 ret. jny. Mon. to Sat.

CANTERBURY & MAIDSTONE
27	E. Bridges	6371 (2-4) 1 sgl. jny. Mon. to Sat.
27	E. Bridges	6304 (4-2) 1 sgl. jny. Mon. to Sat.

CANTERBURY & MARGATE
16	S. Holmans	6297, 6348 (4-5) 2 ret. jnys. daily
16	J. Lowe	6292 (4-2) 1 ret. jny. daily
16	G. Harnett	6312 (4-2) 1 ret. jny. Mon. to Sat.

CANTERBURY & RAMSGATE
17	W. Attwood	6356 (4-2) 1 ret. jny. daily
17	J. Fowler & Co.	6318 (4-5) 1 ret. jny. daily
17	J. Fowler & Co.	6340 (4-11) 1 ret. jny. daily
17	J. Fowler & Co.	6309 (5-1) 1 ret. jny. daily

CANTERBURY & ROCHESTER
27	J. Pettit	6349, 6511 (4-2) 1 ret. jny. daily

CANTERBURY & SITTINGBOURNE
16	T. Ashtell	6290 (3-1) 1 ret. jny. Mon. to Sat.

CANTERBURY & WYE
11	H. Andrews	6280 (4-2) 1 ret. jny. Sat. only

CARLISLE & BRAMPTON
9	E. Fisher	9615 (4-1) 1 ret. jny. Sat. only

CARLISLE & COCKERMOUTH
26	J. Walker	9610 (4—) 1 ret. jny. Tu./Wed., Fri./Sat.

CARLISLE & KENDAL
45	F. Clarke & Co.	9637, 9638 (4-8) 1 ret. jny. Mon. to Sat.

CARLISLE & WHITEHAVEN
42	J. Feather & Co.	9620, 9621 (4-8) 1 ret. jny. Mon. to Sat.

CHALFONT ST. GILES & UXBRIDGE
9   R. Green   10017(4-5) 1 ret. jny. Mon. to Sat.

CHALFORD & WOTTON-UNDER-EDGE
12   W. Chaplin & Co.   7380 (4-5) 1 ret. jny. Sun. only

CHELMSFORD & BRAINTREE
12   S. Brooks   6590 (4-8) 1 ret. jny. Fri. only

CHELTENHAM & BIRKENHEAD
129   J. Jones & Co.   8231 (4-11) 1 sgl. jny. Mon. to Sat.

CHELTENHAM & BROADWAY
16   E. Stephens   7574 (4-5) 1 ret. jny. Tu., Th., Sat.
16   T. Averill   7587 (4-2) 1 ret. jny. Tu., Th., Sat.

CHELTENHAM & CARMARTHEN
120   T. Haines & Co.   7411 (4-8) 1 sgl. jny. Mon. to Sat.
120   G. Davies & Co.   7790 (4-8) 1 sgl. jny. Mon. to Sat.

CHELTENHAM & CIRENCESTER
15   T. Haines & Co.   7350 (2-7) 1 ret. jny. Mon. to Sat.
15   J. Harris   7351 (4-8) 1 ret. jny. Mon. to Sat.

CHELTENHAM & COVENTRY
56   T. Haines & Co.   7382 (4-5) 1 sgl. jny. Mon. to Sat.
54   A. Packwood & Co.   7091 (4-8) 1 sgl. jny. Mon. to Sat.

CHELTENHAM & HANLEY
16   T. Haines   7385 (3-3) 1 sgl. jny. Mon. to Sat.

CHELTENHAM & LEAMINGTON
40   T. Haines & Co.   7433, 7436 (4-5) 1 ret. jny. Mon. to Sat.

CHELTENHAM & MALVERN
24   J. Neyler & Co.   7432 (4-5) 1 ret. jny. Mon. to Sat.
24   J. Pratt   7582 (4-5) 1 ret. jny. Mon. to Sat.

CHELTENHAM & PAINSWICK
10   T. Richins   7352 (3-1) 1 ret. jny. Mon., Tu., Wed., Th., Sat.

CHELTENHAM & PERSHORE
18   J. Goose   7575 (4-8) 1 ret. jny. Th. only

CHELTENHAM & PRESTEIGNE
58   R. Phillips & Co.   7650 (4-5) 1 ret. jny. Mon. to Sat.

CHELTENHAM & ROYAL ROCK FERRY
128   J. Neyler & Co.   7390 (4-8) 1 sgl. jny. Mon. to Sat.
128   B. Bretherton & Co. 8235 (4-8) 1 sgl. jny. Mon. to Sat.

CHELTENHAM & SHREWSBURY
74   J. Neyler & Co.   7428 (4-5) 1 sgl. jny. Mon. to Sat.
73   J. Taylor & Co.   8169 (4-8) 1 sgl. jny. Mon. to Sat.

CHELTENHAM & STROUD
13   J. Bishop & Co.   7359 (3-9) 1 ret. jny. daily

CHELTENHAM & TEWKESBURY
9   J. Davies   7406 (5-4) I ret. jny. Th. only

CHELTENHAM & WINCHCOMBE
7   W. Tustin   7431 (5-4) I ret. jny. Mon., Tu., Th., Fri.

CHESTER & BANGOR
63   J. Jones & Co.   8203, 8204 (4-11) I ret. jny. Mon. to Sat.

CHESTER & BIRKENHEAD
15   J. Jones & Co.   8241 (4-8) I ret. jny. Mon. to Sat.
15   J. Jones & Co.   8200 (4-11) 2 ret. jnys. daily

CHESTER & DRUID
34   S. Chalton & Co.   8208 (4-8) I ret. jny. Tu., Th., Sat.

CHESTER & EASTHAM FERRY
10   R. Smith & Co.   8207 (6 —), 8212 (6 -12), 8213, 8228,
                         8233, 8242 (4-11), 8243 (4-8). 21 ret.
                         jnys. daily

CHESTER & FARNDON
8   G. Lancely   8220 (4 —) I ret. jny. Sat. only

CHESTER & KINGS FERRY
6   J. Lawrence   8362 (4 —) I ret. jny. Mon. to Sat.

CHESTER & OSWESTRY
27   S. Chalton   8361 (4-8) I ret. jny. Mon. to Sat.

CHESTER & PARKGATE
11½   T. Williams   8210 (4-8) I ret. jny. Wed. & Sat.

CHESTER & WARRINGTON
20   J. Jones & Co.   8226 (4-8) I ret. jny. Mon. to Sat.

CHESTER & WOODSIDE FERRY
15   J. Jones & Co.   8201 (4-8) I ret. jny. Mon. to Sat.

CLARE & DUNMOW
19   J. Nelson & Co.   10029 (4-5) I ret. jny. Mon. to Sat.

COLCHESTER & BRAINTREE
15   S. Brooks   6590 (4-8) I ret. jny. Tu., Th., Sat.

COLCHESTER & HADLEIGH
13   J. Shuttleworth   6592 (4-5) I ret. jny. Mon. to Sat.

COLCHESTER & HARWICH
21   H. Coates   6602 (4-5) I ret. jny. daily

COLCHESTER & WALTON
17   J. Smith & Co.   6600 (4-2) I sgl. jny. daily
17   J. Moles   6601 (4 —) I ret. jny. Tu., Th., Sat.

COVENTRY & ATHERSTONE
13   J. Baraclough   7096 (4-5) I ret. jny. daily

COVENTRY & COLESHILL			
10	C. Farr & Co.	7107 (9-3)	1 ret. jny. Fri. only
COVENTRY & DAVENTRY			
19	W. Goodman & Co.	6927 (4-2)	1 ret. jny. Fri. only
COVENTRY & LEAMINGTON			
12	W. Price	7085 (7-5)	1 ret. jny. daily
12	A. Packwood & Co.	7089 (4-8)	2 ret. jnys. daily
12	C. Price & Co.	7090 (4-8)	1 ret. jny. Mon. to Sat.
COVENTRY & LUTTERWORTH			
15	R. Wormleighton	6953 (7-2)	1 ret. jny. Fri. only
COVENTRY & NUNEATON			
8	W. Johnson	7092 (4-2)	1 ret. jny. Mon. to Sat.
DARLINGTON & BARNARD CASTLE			
16	J. Donkin	9712 (6 —)	1 ret. jny. Mon., Wed., Fri.
16	J. Fawcett	9715 (4 —)	1 ret. jny. Mon. to Sat.
DENBIGH & MOLD			
16	J. Catherall & Co.	8353 (4-8)	1 ret. jny. Mon. to Sat.
DENBIGH & RHYL			
11	R. Walker & Co.	8354 (6 —)	1 sgl. jny. Mon. to Sat.
DERBY & ASHBOURNE			
13	J. Thompson	7994 (9 —)	1 ret. jny. Mon. & Fri.
13	J. Mills	8006 (6 —)	1 ret. jny. Sat. only
13	J. Evans	8003 (4 —)	1 ret. jny. Sat. only
DERBY & BELPER			
8	J. Webster	7995 (6-9)	1 ret. jny. Tu. & Fri.
DERBY & BURTON-ON-TRENT			
11	J. Mills	8006 (6 —)	1 ret. jny. Th. only
11	J. Evans	8003 (4 —)	1 ret. jny. Th. only
DERBY & ILKESTON			
10	R. Burrows	8008 (4 —)	1 ret. jny. Fri. only
10	T. Hives & Co.	8002 (4-11)	1 ret. jny. Fri. only
DERBY & LOUGHBOROUGH			
17	J. Stenson	7993 (4-8)	1 ret. jny. daily
DERBY & NEWCASTLE-UNDER-LYME			
36	G. Dawson	7990 (4-8)	1 sgl. jny. Mon. to Sat.
DERBY & UTTOXETER			
18	J. Tranter	8074 (9 —)	1 ret. jny. Tu., Th., Sat.
18	T. Evans	8003 (4 —)	1 ret. jny. Wed. only
DEVIZES & TROWBRIDGE			
10	J. Lucas	6007 (4-5)	1 ret. jny. Th. only
DEVONPORT & LAUNCESTON			
28	M. Broad	5633 (9 —)	1 ret. jny. Tu./Wed., Fri./Sat.

DONCASTER & BARNSLEY
| 15 | J. Dibbs & Co. | 8591 (4-8) | 1 ret. jny. Tu., Th., Sat. |
| 15 | G. Stringer | 8630 (6—) | 1 ret. jny. Tu., Th., Sat. |

DONCASTER & GAINSBOROUGH
| 21 | R. Wood | 7848 (4-5) | 1 ret. jny. Mon. to Sat. |

DONCASTER & NEWARK
| 39 | R. Wilkinson & Co. | 8619 (4-5) | 1 ret. jny. Mon. to Sat. |

DONCASTER & THORNE
10	J. Chantry	8629 (4-8)	1 ret. jny. Sat.
10	G. Mekin	8647 (4-11)	1 ret. jny. Sat.
10	J. Barley	8648 (4-8)	1 ret. jny. Sat.

DONCASTER & TICKHILL
| 7 | J. Storer | 8631 (4-11) | 1 ret. jny. Sat. |

DOVER & ASHFORD
| 23 | F. Packham | 6288 (4-2) | 1 sgl. jny. Mon. to Sat. |
| 23 | J. Kennett | 6301 (6-3) | 1 sgl. jny. Mon. to Sat. |

DOVER & DEAL
| 9 | W. B. Hook | 6286 (6-3) | 1 ret. jny. Mon. to Sat. |

DOVER & HASTINGS
| 45 | J. Back & Co. | 6359 (4-6) | 1 sgl. jny. Mon. to Sat. |
| 45 | S. Johnson | 6307 (3-3) | 1 sgl. jny. Mon. to Sat. |

DOVER & HERNE BAY
| 24 | T. Divers | 6314 (4-5) | 1 sgl. jny. Mon. to Sat. |

DOVER & HYTHE
| 12 | W. Ashtell | 6361 (6—) | 1 ret. jny. Mon. to Sat. |

DOVER & MARGATE
| 26½ | T. Hudson & Co. | 6320, 6324 (4-8) | 2 ret. jnys. Mon. to Sat., 1 ret. jny. alt. Sun. |
| 26½ | J. Fowler | 6325 (4-8), 6333 (4-5) | 2 ret. jnys. Mon. to Sat., 1 ret. jny. alt. Sun. |

DUNMOW & ONGAR
| 14 | J. West & Co. | 6594 (2-4) | 1 ret. jny. Mon. to Sat. |

DURHAM & SUNDERLAND
13	J. Thwaites	9680 (4-11)	1 ret. jny. Mon. to Sat.
13	R. Egerton	9682 (6-9)	1 ret. jny. daily
13	J. Horner	9683 (6-9)	1 ret. jny. daily

EAST GRINSTEAD & GODSTONE
| 10 | J. Eldridge | 10013 (2-4) | 1 ret. jny. Mon. to Sat. |

EAST PECKHAM & TUNBRIDGE WELLS
| 6 | B. W. Horne & Co. | 10054 (4-2) | 1 ret. jny. Mon. to Sat. |

EDENBRIDGE & WESTERHAM
| 6 | J. Nicholson & Co. | 10004 (4—) | 1 sgl. jny. Mon. to Sat. |

EVESHAM & BROADWAY
6	E. Stephens	7574(4-5)	1 ret. jny. Mon. only
6	T. Averill	7587(4-2)	1 ret. jny. Mon. only

EVESHAM & CHIPPING CAMPDEN
11	T. Ellis	7580(4-5)	1 ret. jny. Mon. Only

EVESHAM & FLADBURY
4	W. Curnock	7581(4-2)	1 ret. jny. Mon. only

EVESHAM & TEWKESBURY
14	J. Browett	7410 (9—)	1 ret. jny. Mon. & Fri.

EXETER & BARNSTAPLE
40	J. Cockram & Co.	5570(4-5)	1 sgl. jny. Mon. to Sat.
40	W. Williams	5523 (6—)	1 sgl. jny. Mon. to Sat.

EXETER & BIDEFORD
39	W. Stephens & Co.	5585 (4-5)	1 sgl. jny. Mon. to Sat.

EXETER & BUDLEIGH SALTERTON
14	W. Stephens & Co.	5588(4-5)	1 sgl. jny. daily

EXETER & CHELTENHAM
118	J. Neyler & Co.	7387(4-8)	1 sgl. jny. Mon. to Sat,
111	J. Cockram & Co.	5573(4-8)	1 sgl. jny. Mon. to Sat,

EXETER & DARTMOUTH
37	J. Cockram & Co.	5569(4-5)	1 sgl. jny. Mon. to Sat.
37	W. Stephens & Co.	5583 (4-5)	1 sgl. jny. Mon. to Sat.
37	D. Donovan & Co.	5634(4-4)	1 ret. jny. daily

EXETER & DEVONPORT
50	J. Cockram & Co.	5560,5571(4-8)	1 ret. jny. daily
50	J. Cockram & Co.	5592 (4-8)	1 sgl. jny. Mon. to Sat.
50	W. Stevens & Co.	5584(4-8)	1 sgl. jny. Mon. to Sat.
46	R. Weakley & Co.	5630,5631(4-11)	1 ret. jny. daily

EXETER & EXMOUTH
10	J. Gifford & Co.	5522 (4-8)	1 ret. jny. Mon. to Sat.

EXETER & FALMOUTH
96	J. Cockram & Co.	5565,5578(4-8)	1 ret. jny. Mon. to Sat,
101	W. Stevens & Co.	5582 (4-8)	1 sgl. jny. Mon. to Sat.

EXETER & SIDMOUTH
15	W. Stevens & Co.	5579 (4-5)	1 ret. jny. Mon., Wed., Fri.
15	G. Power	5524(4-5)	1 ret. jny. Tu., Th., Sat.

EXETER & SOUTHAMPTON
109	J. Cockram & Co.	5572,5574(4-5)	1 ret. jny. Mon. to Sat.

EXETER & TEIGNMOUTH
15	H. Veale	5520(4-8)	1 ret. jny. Mon. to Sat.

EXETER & TIVERTON

14	J. Cockram	5566 (4-5)	1 ret. jny. Mon. to Sat.
14	W. Lake	5526 (4-8)	1 ret. jny. Mon., Wed., Fri.

EXETER & TOPSHAM

4	W. Casely	5527 (4-2)	2 ret. jnys. Mon. to Sat.

EXETER & WEYMOUTH

60	G. Scott & Co.	5973 (4-8)	1 sgl. jny. Mon. to Sat.

FELSTEAD & LITTLE WALSHAM

6	S. Hayward	6596 (4-2)	1 ret. jny. Mon. to Sat.

FRIMLEY & BAGSHOT

2½	F. Rickards & Co.	10030 (2-4)	1 ret. jny. Mon. to Sat.

FROME & DEVIZES

18½	R. Gray & Co.	10000 (4-5)	1 ret. jny. Mon. to Sat.

FROME & WARMINSTER

14	J. Smith	5924 (6 —)	1 ret. jny. Sat. only

GAINSBOROUGH & RETFORD

10	M. Clarke	7915 (6 —)	1 ret. jny. Mon. to Sat.

GLOUCESTER & BLAKENEY

15	E. Saunders	7429 (4-3)	1 ret. jny. Mon., Wed., Sat.

GLOUCESTER & BROMSBERROW

12	J. Brooks	7412 (4-2)	1 ret. jny. Mon., Wed., Th., Sat.

GLOUCESTER & BERKELEY

16	J. Mabbett	7414 (3-5)	1 ret. jny. Mon., Wed., Sat.

GLOUCESTER & CHELTENHAM

9	W. Sterrey	7398 (3-9)	1 ret. jny. daily
9	W. Lovesy	7413 (3-6)	1 ret. jny. Mon. to Sat.
9	T. Haines & Co.	7425 (4-8)	2 ret. jnys. Mon. to Sat.
9	R. Dobbins	7403 (5-1)	1 ret. jny. Mon. to Sat.
9	W. Lett	7396 (3-9)	1 ret. jny. daily
9	W. Sterrey	7397 (3-6)	1 ret. jny. Mon. to Sat.

GLOUCESTER & CHEPSTOW

28	T. Heath & Co.	7394 (4-8)	1 sgl. jny. Mon. to Sat.
28	J. Coles	7430 (5-1)	1 ret. jny. Mon./Tu., Th./Fri.

GLOUCESTER & DURSLEY

15	J. Barnett	7424 (5-4)	1 ret. jny. Mon., Wed., Sat.
15	J. Edmonds & Co.	7393 (3-3)	1 ret. jny. Mon., Wed., Sat.

GLOUCESTER & HEREFORD

31	L. Taylor & Co.	7633 (3-6)	1 ret. jny. Tu., Th., Sat.

GLOUCESTER & LEDBURY

16	L. Taylor & Co.	7643 (4-5)	1 ret. jny. Mon., Wed., Fri.

GLOUCESTER & LITTLEDEAN
12	H. Hodges	7399 (8-1) 1 ret. jny. Mon., Wed., Sat.
12	J. Mountjoy	7423 (4-2) 1 ret. jny. Wed. & Sat.

GLOUCESTER & MITCHELDEAN
11	T. Jones	7402 (5-4) 1 ret. jny. Mon., Wed., Sat.

GLOUCESTER & NEWENT
9	J. Gatfield	7395 (3-1) 1 ret. jny. Mon., Wed., Sat.

GLOUCESTER & NEWNHAM
12	R. Johnson	7407 (3-6) 1 ret. jny. Mon. to Sat.
12	J. Hill	7409 (5-4) 1 ret. jny. Mon., Tu., Th., Sat.
12	W. Wilkes	7417 (6 —) 1 ret. jny. Mon., Wed., Sat.

GLOUCESTER & STROUD
12	T. Bradford	7435 (6 —) 1 ret. jny. Mon., Wed., Sat.
12	J. Bishop & Co.	7355 (3-9) 1 ret. jny. Mon. to Sat.

GLOUCESTER & TETBURY
18½	R. Parker & Co.	7388 (4-8) 1 ret. jny. Mon., Wed., Sat.

GLOUCESTER & TEWKESBURY
11	J. Davis	7406 (5-4 Mon. & Wed., 6-6 Sat.) 1 ret. jny. Mon., Wed., Sat.
11	J. Wells	7408 (4-5) 1 ret. jny. Mon. to Sat.

GOSPORT & FAREHAM
5	W. Haysom	6052 (8-1) 1 ret. jny. Mon. to Sat.

GOSPORT & WINCHESTER
50	R. Hyslop & Co.	6063 (3-3) 1 sgl. jny. Mon. to Sat.

GRAVESEND & BROMPTON
9	M. Hopkins	6501 (6-3) 1 ret. jny. daily
9	J. Edwards	6495 (9-6) 2 ret. jnys. daily
9	C. Whatman	6490 (6-3) 1 ret. jny. daily
9	J. Grist	6485 (6-3) 1 ret. jny. daily
9	J. Grist	6525 (5-1) 1 ret. jny. Mon. to Sat.
9	M. Busbridge	6527 (6-3) 2 ret. jnys. daily
9	M. Busbridge	6528, 6529 (8-4) 4 ret. jnys. daily
9	J. Edwards	6506 (7-5) 2 ret. jnys. daily
9	W. Newman	6523 (4-5) 2 ret. jnys. daily
9	C. Whatman	6524 (6-3) 2 ret. jnys. daily

GRAVESEND & CHATHAM
8	W. Farley	6345, 6350 (4-2) 3 ret. jnys. Mon., Tu., Sat., 2 ret. jnys. Wed., Th., Fri, Sun.
8	W. Smith	6346 (1-5) 1 ret. jny. daily
8	H. Eling	6488 (4-2) 1 ret. jny. daily

(continued on next page)

GRAVESEND & CHATHAM — continued

8	A. Norman	6493 (4-2)	1 ret. jny. daily
8	T. Barnard	6496 (4-2)	2 ret. jnys, Mon. to Fri., 1 ret. jny. Sat. & Sun.
8	W. Hoadley	6507 (5-1)	2 ret. jnys, Mon., Tu., Wed., 1 ret. jny. Th., Fri., Sat., Sun.
8	W. Williams	6498 (3-1)	1 ret. jny. Mon., Tu., Th., Sat, Sun.

GRAVESEND & TOWN MALLING

15	T. Richards	6483 (4-2)	1 ret. jny. Mon., Wed., Fri.

GUILDFORD & FARNHAM

10	J. Falkner	6123 (4-2)	1 ret. jny. Wed. & Sat.

HADHAM & HODDESDON

8	R. Fagg & Co.	10002 (4-5)	1 ret. jny. Mon. to Sat.

HALESWORTH & YOXFORD

7	J. Nelson & Co.	10039 (4-2)	1 ret. jny. daily

HALIFAX & BRIGHOUSE

5	S. Waddington	8795 (4-8)	1 ret. jny. Sat. only

HALIFAX & HEBDEN BRIDGE

8	T. Baldwin & Co.	8816 (4-11)	1 ret. jny. Sat. only

HALIFAX & KEIGHLEY

11	J. Walker	8435 (4-8)	1 ret. jny. Sat. only

HALIFAX & PONTEFRACT

31	M. Outhwaite & Co.	8401 (4-5)	1 ret. jny. daily

HALIFAX & TODMORDEN

12	T. Baldwin & Co.	8815 (4-11)	1 ret. jny. Sat. only

HALIFAX & WAKEFIELD

18	J. Bennett	8812 (4-8)	1 ret. jny. Mon. to Sat.

HAREFIELD & UXBRIDGE

4	W. Tollitt	10009 (4-2)	1 ret. jny. daily

HASLINGDEN & BLACKBURN

9	E. Howarth	9451 (9-3)	1 ret. jny. Wed. only
9	W. Boyd	9468 (——6)	1 ret. jny. Wed. only

HASLINGDEN & BOLTON

11	E. Howarth	9451 (9-3)	1 ret. jny. Mon. only

HASTINGS & ASHFORD

34	W. Tabrett & Co.	6504 (4-—)	1 ret. jny. Mon. to Sat.

HATFIELD HEATH & HARLOW

6	W. Low & Co.	6598 (2-2)	1 ret. jny. Mon. to Sat.

HENLEY-ON-THAMES & HIGH WYCOMBE

12	T. Bowling	7215 (4 —)	1 ret. jny. Tu. & Fri.

HEREFORD & ABERGAVENNY
24   J. Barnett & Co.   7640 (4-5) I ret. jny. Mon. to Sat.

HEREFORD & BRECON
35   J. Morgan & Co.   7654 (4-5) I sgl. jny. Mon. to Sat.

HEREFORD & LEOMINSTER
13   J. Hughes   7645 (4-5) I ret. jny. Wed. & Sat.
13   E. Williams   7642 (4-5) I ret. jny. Wed. & Sat.

HEREFORD & MONMOUTH CAP
12   J. Barnett   7647 (9 —) I ret. jny. Sat. only
12   J. Higley   7646 (4-2) I ret. jny. Wed. & Sat.
12   J. Blackwell   7648 (4-2) I ret. jny. Wed. & Sat.

HEREFORD & WEOBLEY
12   F. Evans   7653 (4-5) I ret. jny. Mon., Wed., Sat.

HEXHAM & BELLINGHAM
14   J. Douglass & Co.   9831 (4-8) I ret. jny. Mon. to Sat.

HIGH WYCOMBE & UXBRIDGE
14   W. Tollitt   10012 (4-8) I ret. jny. Mon. to Sat.
14   W. Tollitt   10019 (4-11) I ret. jny. daily

HOLYWELL & EARTHAM
20   R. Smith & Co.   8355 (4-11) I ret. jny. Mon. to Sat.

HOLYWELL & WOODSIDE
28   J. Poole & Co.   8234 (4-11) I ret. jny. Mon. to Sat.

HORNCASTLE & WRAGBY
10   J. Auckland   7855 (4-2) I ret. jny. Mon. to Sat.

HUDDERSFIELD & HOLMFIRTH
6   N. Batley   8821 (8—1) I ret. jny. Tu. only

HUDDERSFIELD & WAKEFIELD
14   H. C. Lacy & Co.   8834 (4-11) I ret. jny. Mon. to Sat.
14   T. Dunnill   8799 (4-5) I ret. jny. Tu. only

HULL & BEVERLEY
9   R. Procter & Co.   8515 (6-9) I ret. jny. daily
9   D. Morley   8537 (6-12) I ret. jny. daily
9   W. Wilson   8527 (4-14) I ret. jny. daily
9   R. Chaffer   8519 (6-12) I ret. jny. daily
9   D. Morley   8538 (18 —) I ret. jny. Tu. only
9   R. Chaffer   8540 (6-9) I ret. jny. alt. Wed.
9   W. Wilson   8535 (4-11) I ret. jny. Mon. & Sun.

HULL & BRIDLINGTON QUAY
34   R. Chaffer & Co.   8534 (4-8) I ret. jny. Mon. to Sat.

HULL & COTTINGHAM
5   W. Allison   8544 (6-9) I ret. jny. Mon. to Sat.
5   R. J. Atkinson & Co.   8510 (6-9) 2 ret. jnys. daily

HULL & HESSLE		
4	E. Miles	8518 (4-5) 2 ret. jnys. Mon. to Sat.

HULL & HORNSEA		
16	R. Procter & Co.	8532 (4-11) I sgl. jny. Mon. to Sat.
16	R. Chaffer & Co.	8533 (4-5) I ret. jny. Mon. to Sat.

HULL & MALTON		
40	P. Ashton & Co,	8517 (15 —) I ret. jny. Mon./Tu., Th./Fri.

HULL & NORTH CAVE		
14	E. Miles	8539 (4-8) I ret. jny. Mon. to Sat.
14	R. Chaffer	8513 (4-8) I ret. jny. Mon. to Sat.

HULL & PATRINGTON		
15	J. Wing	8529 (8-10) I ret. jny. Tu. only
15	J. Wing	8530 (4-5) I ret. jny. Th. only

HULL & SCARBOROUGH		
53	R. Chaffer & Co.	8520, 8873 (4-11) I ret. jny. Mon. to Sat.
53	J. Hammond & Co.	8874 (4-11) I ret. jny. Mon. to Sat.

HULL & SELBY		
34	C. Marshall & Co.	8511 (4-8) I ret. jny. Mon. to Sat.

HULL & SWANLAND		
7	T. Tillingham	8512 (9 —) I ret. jny. daily

HUNGERFORD & SWINDON		
16	W. Halcomb & Co.	6009 (4-5) I sgl. jny. Mon. to Sat.

HUNTINGDON & RAMSEY		
12	S. Beard	6865 (6 —) I ret. jny. Sat. only
12	J. Cox	6864 (6 —) I ret. jny. Sat. only

IPSWICH & BURY ST. EDMUNDS		
25½	J. Deck & Co.	6662, 6663 (4-8) 2 ret. jnys. daily

IPSWICH & COLCHESTER		
18	J. Spurling	6671 (4-2) I ret. jny. Mon. to Sat.
19	R. Wilson	6673 (4-5) I ret. jny. Mon. to Sat.

IPSWICH & SCOLE		
43	T. Wiggins & Co.	6766 (4-5) I ret. jny. daily

IPSWICH & WICKHAM MARKET		
12	J. Haxell & Co.	6670 (4-5) I ret. jny. Mon. to Sat.

KENDAL & MILNTHORPE		
8	J. Jackson	9624 (4-5) I ret. jny. Wed., Fri., Sun.

KIDDERMINSTER & BRECON		
64	C. Radenhurst & Co.	7528 (4-8) I sgl. jny. Mon., Wed., Fri.

KIDDERMINSTER & STOURBRIDGE		
7	J. Gardener	7513 (4-2) I ret. jny. Mon., Tu., Wed., Th., Sat.

KIDDERMINSTER & STOURPORT		
4	J. Purser	7521 (6-3) I ret. jny. Th. only

KIRKDALE & OLD SWAN
5½ M. Dickinson & Co.   9461(8-4) 4 ret. jnys. Mon. only

KNARESBOROUGH & LOW HARROGATE
4   T. Thackberray   8886 (4-5) I ret. jny. Mon. to Sat.

LANCASTER & BARNARD CASTLE
60 J. Dunn & Co.   9581, 9586 (4-5) I ret. jny. daily

LANCASTER & KENDAL
21 T. Fisher & Co.   9628 (4-7) I ret. jny. Mon. to Sat.

LANCASTER & PRESTON
22 J. Dunn & Co.   9589 (4-8) I ret. jny. Mon. to Sat.

LANCASTER & ULVERSTON
21 J. Dunn & Co.   9580 (4-8) I ret. jny. daily
21 J. Ashburne   9588 (4-2) I sgl. jny. Tu. to Sun.

LEAMINGTON & STRATFORD-UPON-AVON
10 W. Gibbs & Co.   7067 (4-5) I ret. jny. Mon. to Sat.

LEEDS & BRADFORD
10 T. Bradford   8827 (4-11) I ret. jny. Mon. to Sat.
10 R. Shilburn   8394 (4-11) I ret. jny. Mon. to Sat.
10 J. Wood   8806 (4-11) I ret. jny. daily
10 J. Wood & Co.   8800 (4-8) I ret. jny. daily
10 J. Frances   8418 (4-11) I ret. jny. Th.
10 S. Yates   8426 (4-11) I ret. jny. daily
10 J. Wood   8408 (4-11) I ret. jny. daily

LEEDS & BRAMLEY
4   J. Shires   8397 (5-4) 2 ret. jnys. Tu. & Sat.

LEEDS & CLECKHEATON
9   W. Varley   8421 (9—) I ret. jny. Tu., Wed., Fri., Sat.

LEEDS & DEWSBURY
9   T. Wormald   8826 (4-11) I ret. jny. Tu., Wed., Sat.

LEEDS & GUISLEY
9   J. Smith   8399 (6—) I ret. jny. Tu. & Sat.

LEEDS & HALIFAX
14 J. Carr & Co.   8791 (4-8) I ret. jny. Mon. to Sat.
18 W. Lee & Co.   8405 (4-11) I ret. jny. Mon. to Sat.

LEEDS & HECKMONDWIKE
8   W. Jewison   8444 (12—) I ret. jny. Tu., Wed., Fri., Sat.

LEEDS & HUDDERSFIELD
15 C. Sykes & Co.   8803 (4-5) I ret. jny. Mon. to Sat.
15 M. Outhwaite   8409 (4-11) I ret. jny. Mon. to Sat.

LEEDS & KENDAL
76 M. Outhwaite & Co. 8406 (4-11) I sgl. jny. Mon. to Sat.
76 J. Jackson & Co.   9625 (4-11) I sgl. jny. Mon. to Sat.

LEEDS & KIRKSTALL

2½	J. Dawkes	8395 (6—)	4 ret. jnys. Tu., 5 ret. jnys. Sat.
2½	R. Johnson	8392 (6—)	4 ret. jnys. Tu., 6 ret. jnys. Sat.

LEEDS & KNARESBOROUGH

| 18 | T. Pearson & Co. | 8872 (4-11) | 1 ret. jny. Mon. to Sat. |

LEEDS & OXLEY

| 10 | T. Prockter | 8396 (4-8) | 1 ret. jny. Tu. & Sat. |

LEEDS & PONTEFRACT

| 13 | W. Wood | 8437 (4-11) | 1 ret. jny. daily |
| 13 | J. Shaw | 8400 (4-11) | 1 ret. jny. Mon. to Sat. |

LEEDS & PRESTON

| 63 | M. Outhwaite & Co. | 8402 (4-8) | 1 sgl. jny. Mon. to Sat. |
| 63 | E. Clough & Co. | 8962 (4-8) | 1 sgl. jny. Mon. to Sat. |

LEEDS & RAILWAY DEPOT

| 1 | J. Atkinson & Co. | 8438 (12—) | 3 ret. jnys. Mon. to Sat., 1 ret. jny. Sun. |

LEEDS & RIPON

| 26 | J. Frances & Co. | 8417 (4-11) | 1 ret. jny. Mon. to Sat. |

LEEDS & THORP ARCH

| 12 | W. Adkin | 8398 (6-3) | 1 ret. jny. Tu., Th., Sat. |

LEEDS & WAKEFIELD

9	T. Dunnill	8818 (4-11)	1 ret. jny. daily
9	T. Brayshaw	8425 (4-11)	1 ret. jny. Mon. to Sat.
9	W. Watson & Co.	8793 (4-8)	1 ret. jny. Mon. to Sat.
9	W. Watson	8811 (4-11)	1 ret. jny. Mon. to Sat.
9	J. Herfield & Co.	8415 (4-11)	1 ret. jny. daily
9	W. Lee & Co.	8414 (4-11)	1 ret. jny. Mon. to Sat.

LEEDS & YEADON

| 8 | E. Boyne | 8429 (4-8) | 1 ret. jny. Tu. & Sat. |

LEEDS & YORK

24	W. Lee & Co.	8413 (6-12)	1 ret. jny. Mon. to Sat.
24	J. Barber & Co.	8726 (4-11)	1 ret. jny. Mon. to Sat.
26	J. Barber & Co.	8736 (4-11)	1 ret. jny. Mon. to Sat.
24	R. Cattle & Co.	8738 (4-11)	1 ret. jny. Mon. to Sat.

LEICESTER & BURTON-ON-TRENT

| 26 | C.S. Pettifor & Co. | 6958 (4-5) | 1 ret. jny. daily |

LEICESTER & COVENTRY

| 26 | J. Briggs & Co. | 6972 (4-8) | 1 ret. jny. Mon. to Sat. |

LEICESTER & GRANTHAM

| 31 | G. Harston | 7835 (2-2) | 1 ret. jny. Mon./Tu., Th./Fri. |

LEICESTER & HINCKLEY

| 13 | W. Tomlinson | 6960 (4-8) | 1 ret. jny. Tu. & Sat. |

LEICESTER & HUSBANDS BOSWORTH
14   J. Adams   6952 (6-3)   1 ret. jny. Wed. & Sat.

LEICESTER & LOUGHBOROUGH
11   T. Hudson & Co.   6961 (4-8)   1 ret. jny. Sat. only
11   G. Roe   6951 (2-4)   1 ret. jny. daily
11   J. Taylor & Co.   6967 (3-6)   1 ret. jny. Th. only
11   J. Mitchell   6954 (7-2)   1 ret. jny. daily
11   G. Roe   6968 (7-2)   1 ret. jny. Mon. to Sat.
13   R. Wormlighton   6953 (7-2)   1 ret. jny. Wed. & Sat.
13   W. Scott   6069 (3-6)   1 ret. jny. Th. only

LEICESTER & MARKET HARBOROUGH
15   C. Gibbs   6962 (4-8)   1 ret. jny. Mon., Wed., Sat.

LEICESTER & MELTON MOWBRAY
15   J. Briggs & Co.   6950 (6-3)   1 ret. jny. Mon. to Sat.
15   W. Scott & Co.   6969 (9-)   1 ret. jny. Tu. only

LEICESTER & NORTHAMPTON
31   J. Taylor & Co.   6967 (3-6)   1 ret. jny. Mon., Wed., Sat.

LEICESTER & SOUTHAM
30   J. Briggs & Co.   6956 (4-5)   1 ret. jny. Mon. to Sat.

LEIGH & SALFORD
12   M. Kirkman   9435 (4-12)   1 ret. jny. Tu. only
12   M. Kirkman   9436 (4-8)   1 ret. jny. Sat. only

LEOMINSTER & PRESTEIGNE
14   R. Coates   7635 (2-2)   1 sgl. jny. Mon. to Sat.

LICHFIELD & TAMWORTH
7   J. Clarke & Co.   7108 (4-5)   1 sgl. jny. Fri. only

LIMPSFIELD & GODSTONE
3½   J. Eldridge   10014 (2-2)   1 ret. jny. daily

LINCOLN & GAINSBOROUGH
18   T. H. Dobbs & Co.   7827 (4-8)   1 ret. jny. Mon. to Sat.
18   J. Stephenson & Co.   7823 (4-5)   1 ret. jny. Mon. to Sat.

LINCOLN & LEICESTER
55   C. S. Pettifor & Co.   6959 (4-8)   1 ret. jny. Mon. to Sat.

LINCOLN & LOUTH
26   W. Dawbee & Co.   7828 (4-5)   1 ret. jny. Mon. to Sat.
34   W. Spratt & Co.   7853 (4-8)   1 ret. jny. Mon. to Sat.

LINCOLN & NEWARK
16   J. Stephenson & Co.   7841 (4-5)   1 ret. jny. Mon. to Sat.

LINCOLN & NEW HOLLAND FERRY
36   B. Nicholson & Co.   7846, 7849 (4-8)   1 ret. jny. daily
36   B. Nicholson & Co.   7842 (4-5)   1 ret. jny. Mon. to Sat.

LIVERPOOL & AIGBURTH
4   R. Church   9464 (10-2) 2 ret. jnys. Mon. to Sat., I ret. jny.
                                              Sun.

LIVERPOOL & AINTREE
6½   B. Bretherton   9400 (14-1) 4 ret. jnys. Mon. only

LIVERPOOL & BIRMINGHAM
94   B. Bretherton & Co. 7045, 9404 (4-8) I ret. jny. Mon. to Sat.
96   B. Bretherton & Co. 7110, 9402 (4-8) I ret. jny. daily
97   B. Bretherton & Co. 7036, 9401 (4-8) I ret. jny. daily

LIVERPOOL & CHELTENHAM
130 J. Neyler & Co.   7440 (4-11) I sgl. jny. Mon. to Sat.

LIVERPOOL & CROSBY VILLAGE
7   S. Towers   9418, 9421, 9424 (12-6) 5 ret. jnys. daily
7   J. Newton   9465 (8-4) I ret. jny. Mon. to Sat, 2 ret. jnys.
                                              Sun.

LIVERPOOL & FAIRFIELD TERRACE
2   J. Bellis   9473 (8-4) 5 ret. jnys. Mon. to Sat.

LIVERPOOL & KIRKDALE
2   W. Bushby & Co.   9433 (10-5) I ret. jny. Mon. to Sat.

LIVERPOOL & LANCASTER
53   B. Bretherton & Co. 9450 (4-11) I ret. jny. Mon. to Sat.

LIVERPOOL & MANCHESTER
36   T. Coxon & Co.   8968 (4-8) I ret. jny. daily

LIVERPOOL & ORMSKIRK
13   G. Proffitt   9414 (4-8) I ret. jny. Wed. & Sat.
13   J. Morris   9432 (4-8) I ret. jny. Wed. & Sat.

LIVERPOOL & PRESCOT
7½   J. Dutton   9415 (10-5) I ret. jny. daily

LIVERPOOL & PRESTON
31   J. Strange & Co.   9410, 9411 (4-11) 2 ret. jnys. Mon. to Sat, I ret.
                                              jny. Sun.
31   J. Strange & Co.   9413 (4-8) I ret. jny. Mon. to Sat.
31   J. Weatherald & Co. 9470 (4-8) I ret. jny. Mon. to Sat.
31   B. Bretherton & Co. 9406 (4-11) I ret. jny. Tu., Th., Sat.
31   B. Bretherton & Co. 9475 (4-11) I ret. jny. Mon. to Sat.

LIVERPOOL & RAILWAY STATION
1¼   P. Eastwood & Co.   9426 (12-6) 4 ret. jnys. Mon. to Sat, 2 ret. jnys. Sun.
1¼   P. Eastwood & Co.   9427 (17-1) 4 ret. jnys. Mon. to Sat, 2 ret. jnys. Sun.
1¼   P. Eastwood & Co.   9456 (12-3) 2 ret. jnys. Mon. to Sat, I ret. jny. Sun.
1¼   B. Bretherton   9422 (14-1) 4 ret. jnys. Mon. to Sat., 2 ret. jnys. Sun.
1¼   B. Bretherton   9423 (11-4) 4 ret. jnys. Mon. to Sat., 2 ret. jnys. Sun.

LIVERPOOL & ST. HELENS		
11	E. Fidler	9412 (4-8) 1 ret. jny. Mon. to Sat.

LIVERPOOL & SOUTHPORT		
21	B. Bretherton & Co.	9477 (4-8) 1 ret. jny. Mon. to Sat.

LIVERPOOL & WELSHPOOL		
59	J. Whitehall & Co.	8360 (4-11) 1 sgl. jny. Mon. to Sat.

LIVERPOOL & WIGAN		
22	J. Milligan	9476 (4-8) 1 ret. jny. Mon. to Sat.

LIVERPOOL & WOOLTON		
5	R. Hill	9419 (12-9) 1 ret. jny. Mon. to Sat, 2 ret. jnys. Sun.
5	R. Hill	9474 (8-4) 1 ret. jny. Mon. to Sat, 2 ret. jnys. Sun.

LOUGHBOROUGH & ASHBY-DE-LA-ZOUCH		
12	T. Hudson & Co.	6961 (4-8) 1 ret. jny. Wed. & Sat.

LOUTH & GRIMSBY		
16	R. Stones	7820 (4-11) 1 ret. jny. Mon. to Sat.
16	J. Wheatley	7850 (9—) 1 ret. jny. Mon. to Sat.

LUDLOW & BRIMFIELD		
4½	H. Godfrey & Co.	7510 (2-4) 1 sgl. jny. Mon. to Sat.

LUDLOW & LEOMINSTER		
13	J. Hughes	7645 (4-5) 2 ret. jnys. Mon. only
10	E. Williams	7642 (4-5) 2 ret. jnys. Mon. only

LYNN & HEACHAM		
14	W. Robertson	6806 (4—) 1 ret. jny. Tu., Th., Sat.
14	R. High	6804 (4—) 1 ret. jny. Mon., Wed., Fri.

LYNN & HUNSTANTON		
18	R. High	6804 (4—) 1 ret. jny. Tu., Th., Sat.

LYNN & SNETTISHAM		
11	A. Smith	6807 (4—) 1 ret. jny. Tu., Th., Sat.

LYNN & STAMFORD		
50	J. Binge & Co.	7838 (4-5) 1 ret. jny. Mon. to Sat.

LYNN & WELLS		
32	G. Cutting & Co.	6802 (4-8) 1 ret. jny. Tu., Th., Sat.

LYNN & WISBECH		
13	T. Martin	6805 (4—) 1 ret. jny. Mon., Wed., Sat.
14	J. Willisee	6800 (4—) 1 ret. jny. Mon. to Sat.

MACCLESFIELD & LEEK		
12	J. Loundes & Co.	8077 (4-4) 1 ret. jny. Tu., Th., Sat.

MAIDSTONE & ASHFORD		
18	C.S. Benton & Co.	6355 (6-3) 2 ret. jnys. Mon. to Sat.

MAIDSTONE & BROMPTON		
10	J. Burch	6514 (4-2) 1 ret. jny. Mon., Wed., Fri.

MAIDSTONE & CHATHAM

9	J. Burch	6515 (4-11)	1 ret. jny. Mon. to Sat.
9	J. Burch	6516 (4-8)	1 ret. jny. Tu., Th., Sat., Sun.
9	J. Burch	6517 (4-8)	1 ret. jny. daily
9	J. Burch	6518 (8-4)	1 ret. jny. Mon. to Sat.

MAIDSTONE & CRANBROOK

14	B. Taylor	6503 (4-2)	1 ret. jny. Mon. to Sat.

MAIDSTONE & GRAVESEND

16	T. Bines	6347 (4-3)	1 ret. jny. daily
16	T. Bines	6520 (8-4)	1 ret. jny. daily
16	J. Grist	6489 (8-4)	1 ret. jny. daily

MAIDSTONE & HASTINGS

38	H. Stickells	6237 (4-2)	1 sgl. jny. Mon. to Sat.

MAIDSTONE & SITTINGBOURNE

11	J. Richardson	6508 (3-1)	1 ret. jny. Mon. to Sat.

MAIDSTONE & TENTERDEN

18	J. Barham	6502 (6-3)	1 ret. jny. Mon. to Sat.

MAIDSTONE & TONBRIDGE

14	W. Clapson	6509 (4-2)	1 ret. jny. Mon. to Sat.

MAIDSTONE & TUNBRIDGE WELLS

20	H. Knight	6505 (4-)	1 ret. jny. Mon. to Sat.

MAIDSTONE & WESTERHAM

22	J. Richards	6499 (3-1)	1 sgl. jny. Mon. to Sat.
23	W. Pearce	6342 (4-8)	1 ret. jny. Mon. to Sat.

MAIDSTONE & YALDING

6	T. Roaff	6513 (4-)	1 ret. jny. Th. only

MANCHESTER & ALTRINCHAM

8	J. Howarth	8238 (6-12)	1 ret. jny. Mon. to Sat.
8	B. Beardman	8225 (6-9)	1 ret. jny. Mon. to Sat.

MANCHESTER & ASHTON-UNDER-LYNE

7	J. Bromley & Co.	8922 (4-11)	2 ret. jnys. daily
7	J. Bromley & Co.	8923 (6-9)	1 ret. jny. daily ex. Fri.
7	J. Bromley & Co.	8924 (4-2)	2 ret. jnys. daily
7	J. Bromley & Co.	8925 (4-11)	2 ret. jnys. daily
7	J. Bromley & Co.	8926 (4-8)	1 ret. jny. daily
7	J. Bromley & Co.	8927 (4-8)	1 ret. jny. Tu., Wed., Sat., Sun.

MANCHESTER & BACUP

18	T. Horrocks & Co.	9025 (4-8)	1 ret. jny. Tu. & Sat.
20	J. Haslam	9031 (4-8)	1 ret. jny. Tu. & Sat.

MANCHESTER & BARNSLEY

36	T. Sheppley	8637 (4-8)	1 sgl. jny. Mon. to Sat.

MANCHESTER & BARTON
5	W. Phillips	9139 (8-5) 2 ret. jnys. daily

MANCHESTER & BESS O TH' BARN
5	J. Bell	8906 (8-4) 2 ret. jnys. daily
4	S. Kent	9043 (8-4) 2 ret. jnys. Mon., Wed., Fri., 3 ret. jnys. Tu., Th., Sat., 4 ret. jnys. Sun.

MANCHESTER & BIRMINGHAM
82	J. Weatherald & Co.	9147 (4-11) 1 sgl. jny. daily
82	J. Weatherald & Co.	9164, 9165 (4-11) 1 sgl. jny. Mon. to Sat.
86	J. Webster & Co.	9174 (4-11) 1 sgl. jny. daily
86	C. Stovin & Co.	7018 (4-11) 1 sgl. jny. daily
83	T. Chapman & Co.	7023 (4-11) 1 sgl. jny. Mon. to Sat.
83	T. Chapman & Co.	7039 (4-11) 1 sgl. jny. daily
84	T. Waddell & Co.	7062 (4-11) 1 sgl. jny. Mon. to Sat.

MANCHESTER & BLACKBURN
23½	J. Watson	9440 (10-5) 1 ret. jny. Tu. only
23½	W. Frankland & Co.	9405 (8-4) 1 ret. jny. Tu. only
25	J. Chadwick & Co.	8954 (4-11) 1 ret. jny. daily
25	J. Chadwick & Co.	8953 (4-8) 1 ret. jny. Mon., Wed., Fri.
25	J. Wilding & Co.	8998 (4-11) 1 ret. jny. daily
25	J. Wilding & Co.	8999 (4-11) 1 ret. jny. Tu. only
22	T. Lees & Co.	9047 (4-8) 1 ret. jny. Mon., Wed., Th., Sat., Sun.
25	R. Taylor	9096 (4-11) 1 ret. jny. daily

MANCHESTER & BOLTON
11	E. Buckle	8931 (4-8) 1 ret. jny. Tu. & Sat.
11	E. Buckle	8932 (4-8) 1 ret. jny. Tu. only
11	J. Greenwood & Co.	8993 (4-11) 1 ret. jny. Tu., Wed., Th., Sat.
11	J. Greenwood & Co.	8994 (4-8) 1 ret. jny. daily
11	T. Lees & Co.	9046 (4-11) 1 ret. jny. Tu., Th., Sat.
11	T. Telford	9100 (4-8) 1 ret. jny. daily
11	T. Telford	9101 (4-8) 1 ret. jny. Mon. to Sat.
11	S. Eyre & Co.	8982 (4-8) 2 ret. jnys. daily

MANCHESTER & BRADFORD
40	J. Carr & Co.	8796 (4-11) 1 ret. jny. Mon. to Sat.

MANCHESTER & BROUGHTON
2	J. Amos & Co.	8900 (8-4) 4 ret. jnys. Mon. to Sat.
2	J. Amos & Co.	8901 (6-3) 6 ret. jnys. Mon. to Sat.
2	J. Bell	8904 (8-4) 3 ret. jnys. Mon. to Sat., 2 ret. jnys. Sun.
2	A. Cornthwaite & Co.	8970 (8-1) 3 ret. jnys. Mon. to Sat., 1 ret. jny. Sun.

MANCHESTER & BURNAGE		
10½	R. Mellor	9060 (4-8) I ret. jny. Tu.& Sat.

MANCHESTER & BURNLEY		
24	J. Chadwick & Co.	8952 (4-11) I ret. jny. Tu. only

MANCHESTER & BURY		
8	W. Hardman	9014 (4-8) I ret. jny. Mon. to Sat., 2 ret. jnys. Sun.
8	W. Hardman	9015 (4-11) I ret. jny. Tu.& Sat.
8	T. Hall	9024 (4-8) I ret. jny. Tu., Wed., Th., Sat.
8	J. Ramsbottom	9076 (4-8) 2 ret. jnys. daily
8	J. Ramsbottom	9077 (4-8) 2 ret. jnys. daily
8	J. Ramsbottom	9078 (6-9) 2 ret. jnys. Tu. to Sun.
8	J. Ramsbottom	9079 (6-9) I ret. jny. Tu. & Sun.
8	E. Gilding	9124 (4-8) I ret. jny. Tu. & Sun.
8	E. Gilding	9125 (4-8) I ret. jny. Tu., Th., Sat.

MANCHESTER & BUXTON		
24	C.H. Lacy & Co.	9149 (4-8) I ret. jny. Mon. to Sat.

MANCHESTER & CARLISLE		
119	J. Webster & Co.	9177 (4-11) I sgl. jny. daily
120	J. Feather & Co.	9633 (4-11) I sgl. jny. daily

MANCHESTER & CHEADLE		
7	W. Davies	8974 (6-9) I ret. jny. Mon., Tu., Th., Sat.

MANCHESTER & CHEETHAM		
2	J. Ramsbottom	9070, 9071, 9072, 9073 (8-4) 27 ret. jnys. Mon., Tu., Sat., 25 ret. jnys. Wed., Th., Fri., 12 ret. jnys. Sun.
2	J. Ramsbottom ⎫ J. Robinson ⎭	9074, 9075 (6-3) 12 ret. jnys. Mon., Tu., Wed., Sat., 11 ret. jnys. Th., Fri., 4 ret. jnys, Sun.

MANCHESTER & CHESTER		
39	J. Jones & Co.	8205, 8237 (4-8) I ret. jny. Mon. to Sat.
39	S. Chalton & Co.	8248 (4-8) I sgl. jny. Mon. to Sat., I ret. jny. Sun.
38	C.H. Lacy & Co.	9154 (4-8) I sgl. jny. Mon. to Sat.

MANCHESTER & CHORLEY		
22	W. Sanson	9094 (6-6) I ret. jny. Tu.

MANCHESTER & CHORLTON		
1½	J. Buck	8903 (8-4) 13 ret. jnys. Mon. to Sat.

MANCHESTER & CLITHEROE		
30	J. Chadwick & Co.	8955 (4-11) I ret. jny. Tu. to Sat., I sgl. jny. Sun. & Mon.

MANCHESTER & COLNE
30   J.Chadwick & Co.   8951(4-11) I ret.jny. Tu.,Wed.,Th, Sat., I sgl. jny. Fri.& Sun.

MANCHESTER & CONGLETON
26   J.Weatherald & Co. 9162(4-11) I ret.jny. Mon. to Sat.

MANCHESTER & DERBY
56   W.Robinson & Co. 9082(4-8) I sgl. jny. Mon.to Sat.

MANCHESTER & DIDSBURY
5   W.Winder   9127 (8-4) 2 ret. jnys. Mon.to Sat., I ret. jny. Sun.

5   W.Winder   9128 (11-1) I ret.jny. Mon.to Sat.

MANCHESTER & DUKINFIELD
8   J.Drury   8972(6-3) I ret.jny. Tu.only

8   J.Drury   8973(4-8) I ret.jny. Tu.,Th.,Sat.

MANCHESTER & ECCLES
4   J.Greenwood   8987 (8-4) 9 ret. jnys. Mon.to Sat., 3 ret. jnys. Sat.

MANCHESTER & FAILSWORTH
9   B.B. Robinson   9081 (9-3) 5 ret. jnys. Mon. to Sat., 4 ret. jnys. Sun.

9   G.Trodman   9097 (8-4) 5 ret.jnys. Mon. to Sat., 6 ret. jnys. Sun.

MANCHESTER & GLOSSOP
14   J.Bromley & Co.   8928(4-8) I ret. jny. Sat.& Sun.

MANCHESTER & GOOLE
66   J.Shaw   8432(4-8) I sgl. jny. Mon.to Sat.

66   T.Dunnell & Co.   8820 (4-8) I sgl. jny. Mon. to Sat.

MANCHESTER & GREEN ACRES
8   J.Grindrod   9000(4-8) I ret. jny. daily ex. Fri.

8   J.Grindrod   9001,9002 (4-2) 2 ret.jnys. Tu.& Sat.

8   J.Wild   9132 (4-2) I ret.jny. Tu.,Th, Sat.

8   J.Wild   9133 (4-2) I ret.jny. Tu., Wed., Th., 2 ret. jnys. Sat.

8   J.Wild   9134(6-9) I ret.jny. Tu.,Wed.,Th., Sat., Sun,

MANCHESTER & GREENHEYS
2   C.Batty   8942(8-4) 6 ret. jnys. Mon. to Sat., 2 ret. jnys. Sun.

2   C.Batty   8943(8-4) 4 ret. jnys. Mon. to Sat.

2   B.Karper   9028(8-4) 6 ret. jnys. Mon. to Sat.

MANCHESTER & HALIFAX
27   J.Carr & Co.   8792(4-11) I ret. jny. Mon. to Sat.

25   T.Mann & Co.   8802 (4-11) I ret. jny. daily

MANCHESTER & HARPURHEY
2 W. White 9102(8-4) 4 ret. jnys. Mon. to Sat, 3 ret. jnys. Sun.

MANCHESTER & HAYFIELD
18 R. Quamby 7996(4-8) I ret. jny. Tu. only

MANCHESTER & HEBDEN BRIDGE
24 T. Baldwin & Co. 8816 (4-11) I ret. jny. Tu./Wed.

MANCHESTER & HEY CHAPEL
9 W. Shaw & Co. 9089(6-9) I ret. jny. Tu. & Sat.

MANCHESTER & HEYWOOD
8 T. Battersby 8907(6-12) I ret. jny. Tu., Th., Sat.
8 T. Battersby 8908(4-11) I ret. jny. Tu., Wed., Sat., Sun.
8 T. Battersby 8909(4-8) I ret. jny. Tu. & Sat.
8 J. Hope 9023(6-3) I ret. jny. Tu. & Sat.
8 G. Massey & Co. 9061(6-9) I ret. jny. Tu., Th., Sat.

MANCHESTER & HUDDERSFIELD
24 C.P. Lacy & Co. 9141(4-11) I ret. jny. Mon. to Sat.

MANCHESTER & HULME
2 B. Harper 9029 (8-4) 4 ret. jnys. Mon. to Sat.

MANCHESTER & HYDE
7 S. Perrin 9065 (8-4) 2 ret. jnys. daily
7 J. Spence 9086 (6-9) I ret. jny. Mon. to Sat., 2 ret. jnys. Sun.
7 J. Spence 9087 (6-12) I ret. jny. Tu., Wed., Sat., Sun.

MANCHESTER & LANCASTER
53 J. Dunn & Co. 9583 (4-11) I sgl. jny. Mon. to Sat.
56 H. Catout & Co. 9582 (4-11) I sgl. jny. Mon. to Sat.
52 C.H. Lacy & Co. 9148 (4-11) I sgl. jny. Mon. to Sat.
56 J. Weatherald & Co. 9159 (4-11) I sgl. jny. Mon. to Sat.

MANCHESTER & LANE END
40 J. Webster & Co. 9175 (4-11) I ret. jny. Mon. to Sat.

MANCHESTER & LEEDS
45 J. Carr & Co. 8424(4-11) I sgl. jny. Mon. to Sat.
40 J. Frances & Co. 8419 (4-8) I ret. jny. Mon. to Sat.
40 M. Outhwaite & Co. 8420(4-11) I sgl. jny. Mon. to Sat.
45 M. Outhwaite & Co. 8428(4-11) I sgl. jny. Mon. to Sat.
45 M. Outhwaite & Co. 8427(4-11) I sgl. jny. daily
41 M. Outhwaite & Co. 8407(4-11) I sgl. jny. Mon. to Sat.
50 W. Lee & Co. 8430(4-11) I sgl. jny. Mon. to Sat.
45 D. Hollings & Co. 8422(4-11) I sgl. jny. Mon. to Sat.
41 D. Hollings & Co. 8431(4-11) I sgl. jny. daily

(continued on next page)

MANCHESTER & LEEDS — continued

41	W. Higginson & Co.	9019, 9020 (4-11) I ret. jny. Mon. to Sat.
45	C. H. Lacy & Co.	9140 (4-11) I sgl. jny. Mon. to Sat.
40	C. H. Lacy & Co.	9142, 9151 (4-11) I ret. jny. Mon. to Sat.
45	C. H. Lacy & Co.	9145, 9146 (4-11) I ret. jny. Mon. to Sat.
40	J. Weatherald & Co.	9166, 9167 (4-11) I ret. jny. daily
49	J. Webster & Co.	9170 (4-11) I sgl. jny. Mon. to Sat.

MANCHESTER & LEES

9	R. Kenworthy	9041 (6-9) I ret. jny. Tu. & Sat.

MANCHESTER & LONGSIGHT

2	J. Hewitt	9027 (8-4) 7 ret. jnys. Mon. to Sat.
2	S. Steel	9095 (8-4) 6 ret. jnys. Mon. to Sat.

MANCHESTER & MACCLESFIELD

18	T. Mosely	8245 (4-11) I ret. jny. daily
18	J. Hibbert & Co.	8222 (4-11) I ret. jny. Mon. to Sat.
18	S. Linley & Co.	8223 (4-8) I ret. jny. Mon. to Sat.

MANCHESTER & MELLOR

12	W. Hanney	8007 (6-) I ret. jny. Tu. only

MANCHESTER & MOSLEY

10	J. Winterbottom	9131 (6-9) I ret. jny. Tu. & Sat.

MANCHESTER & NANTWICH

41	J. Weatherald & Co.	9169 (4-8) I ret. jny. Mon., Wed., Fri., Sat.

MANCHESTER & NEWCASTLE-UNDER-LYME

40	W. Deeming & Co.	8975 (4-11) I ret. jny. daily

MANCHESTER & NEW MILLS

14	J. Bradbury & Co.	7998 (4-11) I ret. jny. daily ex. Fri.

MANCHESTER & NEWTON HEATH

2½	B. B. Robinson	9080 (9-3) 5 ret. jnys. daily

MANCHESTER & NORTHWICH

19	J. Winterbottom	8227 (4 —) I ret. jny. Mon., Wed., Fri.
22	J. Webster & Co.	9172 (4-8) I ret. jny. daily

MANCHESTER & NOTTINGHAM

77	J. Hardy & Co.	7931 (4-11) I sgl. jny. daily
70	J. Wilmot & Co.	7912 (4-11) I sgl. jny. daily
77	J. Simpson & Co.	7891, 7892 (4-11) I ret. jny. daily
77	J. Weatherald & Co.	9160 (4-11) I sgl. jny. daily
70	J. Webster & Co.	9176 (4-11) I sgl. jny. daily

MANCHESTER & OLDHAM

7	J. Buckley & Co.	8933 (6-9) 2 ret. jnys. Mon., Tu., Wed., Th., Sat., I ret. jny. Fri. & Sun.
7	J. Buckley & Co.	8934 (4-8) 2 ret. jnys. daily ex. Fri., I ret. jny. Fri.

(continued on next page)

MANCHESTER & OLDHAM — continued
7	J. Buckley & Co.	8940 (4-8) 1 ret. jny. Tu. & Sat.
7	H. Mellor	9056 (4-8) 1 ret. jny. Mon., Wed., Th., Fri., Sat., 2 ret. jnys. Tu. & Sun.
7	H. Mellor	9057 (6-9) 1 ret. jny. Mon., Tu, Wed., Th, Sun, 2 ret. jnys. Sat., no service Fri.

MANCHESTER & PENDLETON
2	J. Greenwood	8988, 8992 (8-4) 30 ret. jnys. Mon. to Sat., 22 ret. jnys. Sun.
2	J. Greenwood	8989, 8990, 8991 (6-3) 22 ret. jnys. Mon. to Sat., 10 ret. jnys. Sun.

MANCHESTER & PRESTON
31	H. Sheldon	9090 (4-8) 1 ret. jny. Mon. to Sat.
31	H. Sheldon	9091 (4-8) 1 ret. jny. Mon., Fri., Sat., 1 sgl. jny. Wed. & Th., no service Tu., Sun.
31	H. Sheldon	9092 (4-8) 1 ret. jny. Tu., 1 sgl. jny. Wed., Th.
31	J. Wilcockson & Co.	9130 (4-11) 1 ret. jny. Mon. to Sat.
31	C.H. Lacy & Co.	9152 (4-11) 1 ret. jny. Mon. to Sat.
31	C.H. Lacy & Co.	9153 (4-8) 1 ret. jny. Mon. to Sat.
34	J. Webster & Co.	9171 (4-8) 1 ret. jny. Mon. to Sat.

MANCHESTER & RAILWAY STATION
½	C.H. Lacy & Co.	9143 (14-1) 4 ret. jnys. Mon. to Sat., 2 ret. jnys. Sun.
½	C.H. Lacy & Co.	9144 (14-1) 4 ret. jnys. Mon. to Sat., 2 ret. jnys. Sun.
½	J. Weatherald & Co.	9163 (14-1) 4 ret. jnys. Mon. to Sat., 2 ret. jnys. Sun.
½	J. Webster & Co.	9173 (14-1) 5 ret. jnys. Mon. to Sat., 2 ret. jnys. Sun.

MANCHESTER & RATCLIFFE
6	R. Howarth	9008 (8-4) 2 ret. jnys. Mon., Wed., Th., Fri., Sun., 3 ret. jnys. Tu. & Sat.

MANCHESTER & ROCHDALE
11	J. Ramsbottom	9078 (6-9) 1 ret. jny. Mon.
11	J. Robinson	9074 (6-3) 1 ret. jny. Mon.
11	J. Ashton	8902 (8-1) 1 ret. jny. Tu. & Sat.
11	J. Haynes	9007 (4-11) 1 ret. jny. Tu., Wed., Th., Sat.
11	J. Haynes	9006 (6-9) 1 ret. jny. Tu., Wed., Th., Sat.
11	W. Barnish & Co.	8944 (4-8) 2 ret. jnys. daily
11	W. Barnish & Co.	8946 (4-8) 1 ret. jny. Tu. & Sat.
11	C.H. Lacy & Co.	9052 (4-8) 2 ret. jnys. daily
11	J. Margetroyd	9055 (4-8) 1 ret. jny. daily

MANCHESTER & ROYTON

8	W. Ogden & Co.	9063 (6-9) I ret. jny. Tu. & Sat.

MANCHESTER & RUSHOLME

2	W. Winder	9135 (8-4) 2 ret. jnys. Mon. to Sat.
2	W. Winder	9126 (8-4) 6 ret. jnys. Mon. to Sat.

MANCHESTER & SETTLE

42	J. Chadwick	8956 (4-11) I ret. jny. Sun./Mon.

MANCHESTER & SHAW

9	R. Mellor	9059 (4-8) I ret. jny. Tu., Th., Sat.
9	J. Humphreys & Co.	9016 (4-8) I ret. jny. Tu. & Sat.

MANCHESTER & SHEFFIELD

40	W. Bradley & Co.	8592 (4-8) I ret. jny. Mon. to Sat.
38	W. Bradley & Co.	8613 (4-11) I sgl. jny. daily
40	W. Bickley & Co.	8623 (4-8) I sgl. jny. daily
40	W. Bickley & Co.	8596 (4-8) I ret. jny. Mon. to Sat.
42	M. Potts & Co.	8655 (4-8) I ret. jny. Mon. to Sat.
40	W. Travis	8611 (4-8) I ret. jny. daily
44	W. Higginson & Co.	9018 (4-8) I ret. jny. Mon. to Sat.
39	C. H. Lacy & Co.	9150 (4-11) I sgl. jny. Mon. to Sat.
38	J. Weatherald & Co.	9161 (4-11) I sgl. jny. Mon. to Sat.

MANCHESTER & SKIPTON

42	J. Chadwick & Co.	8950 (4-11) I ret. jny. Mon., I sgl. jny. Tu., Wed., Fri., Sun.

MANCHESTER & SOUTHPORT

40	T. Howarth	9010 (6-3) I sgl. jny. Mon. to Sat.

MANCHESTER & STALYBRIDGE

8	J. Bromley	8919, 8920 (4-11), 8921 (4-8). 10 ret. jnys. daily

MANCHESTER & STOCKPORT

6	J. Bromley	8910 (6-3) 3 ret. jnys. daily
6	J. Bromley	8911, 8912, 8913, 8914, 8915 (4-2). 15 ret. jnys. daily
6	J. Bromley	8916, 8917, 8918 (6-9) Rtn. jnys: Mon. 4, Tu. 5, Wed. 4, Th. 3, Fri. & Sat. 4, Sun. 6.
6	A. Cornthwaite & Co.	8969 (4-2) 2 ret. jnys. daily
6	A. Cornthwaite & Co.	8970 (8-1) I ret. jny. Sun.
6	A. Cornthwaite & Co.	8971 (6-9) I ret. jny. Tu., Wed., Fri., Sat., Sun.
6	S. Eyre	8980, 8981 (4-2) 2 ret. jnys. daily
6	W. Ramsbottom	9068 (4-8) I ret. jny. Tu., Wed., Sat., Sun.
6	W. Ramsbottom	9069 (4-2) 2 ret. jnys. ex. Wed., I ret. jny. Wed.

continued on next page.

MANCHESTER & STOCKPORT — continued

6	R. Harper	9035 (6-9) 1 ret. jny. Mon. to Sat, 2 ret. jnys. Sun.
6	R. Harper	9037 (4-11) 1 ret. jny. Mon. to Sat, 2 ret. jnys. Sun.
6	R. Harper	9036, 9038, 9039, 9040 (4-2) 8 ret. jnys. daily

MANCHESTER & STONY KNOLLS

2	J. Bell	8905 (4-2) 3 ret. jnys. Mon. to Sat., 2 ret. jnys. Sun.

MANCHESTER & STRETFORD

4	G. Todman	9098 (8-4) 5 ret. jnys. Mon. to Sat, 4 ret. jnys. Sun.

MANCHESTER & SWINTON

4	J. Greenwood	8986 (8-4) 3 ret. jnys. Mon. to Sat., 2 ret. jnys. Sun.

MANCHESTER & TODMORDEN

20	T. Baldwin & Co.	8815 (4-11) 1 ret. jny. Tu. only

MANCHESTER & WARRINGTON

18	J. Weatherald & Co.	9168 (4-8) 1 ret. jny. Mon. to Sat.

MANCHESTER & WATER MILL

8	J. Buckley & Co.	8935, 8936, 8937, 8938, 8939 (6-9) 3 ret. jnys. Wed, Th., Fri., Sun, 4 ret. jnys. Mon., 6 ret. jnys. Tu. & Sat.
8	R. Steele	9088 (14-1) 1 ret. jny. Tu.
8	J. Lawton	9050 (6-9) 1 ret. jny. Tu. & Sat.

MANCHESTER & WHITWORTH

14	J. Lomax	9051 (4-8) 1 ret. jny. Tu. & Sat.

MANCHESTER & WIGAN

18	W. Sleddon	9409 (4-11) 1 ret. jny. Tu.

MANCHESTER & WILMSLOW

12	J. Massey	9058 (6-9) 1 ret. jny. Tu., Th., Sat.

MANCHESTER & WORSELEY

4	J. Brooks	8945 (8-4) 2 ret. jnys. Mon. to Sat.

MANSFIELD & RETFORD

20	S. Lowe	7904 (4-2) 1 ret. jny. Mon. to Sat.

MARGATE & DEAL

13	B. W. Hook	6364 (4-8) 1 ret. jny. Mon. to Sat.

MARGATE & HERNE BAY

16	W. Harnett & Co.	6376 (6 —) 1 ret. jny. daily

MARGATE & RAMSGATE

4½	J. Smith	6323 (4-5) 1 ret. jny. daily
4½	J. Smith	6339 (4-2) 1 ret. jny. daily

continued on next page

MARGATE & RAMSGATE — continued

4½	J. Fowler & Co.	6327(6-6)	2 ret. jnys. daily
4½	J. Gell & Co.	6338(4 —)	2 ret. jnys. daily
4½	T. Hudson	6321(5-1)	2 ret. jnys. daily
4½	C. Carlton	6316(4-2)	2 ret. jnys. Mon. to Sat.
4½	W. Fenley	6296(3-1)	1 ret. jny. daily
4½	S. Holmans	6293(4-5)	2 ret. jnys. daily
4½	T. Hudson	6291(5-1)	2 ret. jnys. daily
4½	T. Hudson	6289(4-2)	2 ret. jnys. daily

MARGATE & SANDWICH

4	E. Appleton	6284(4 —)	1 ret. jny. daily

MARYPORT & WIGTON

16	W. Irwin	9617 (4 —)	1 ret. jny. Tu. only

MOLD & EASTHAM FERRY

17	R. Smith & Co.	8210(4-11)	1 ret. jny. Mon. to Sat.

MONKWEARMOUTH & HARTLEPOOL

20	R. Wellis	9855(4-2)	1 ret. jny. daily

MONMOUTH & ROSS

10	J. Barratt	7639 (4-5)	1 ret. jny. Mon. to Sat.

MORPETH & BEDLINGTON

5	W. Darling & Co.	9874(4-11)	1 ret. jny. Wed. only

MORPETH & CHESTER-LE-STREET

22	W. Halliday & Co.	9876(4 —)	1 ret. jny. Tu./Wed.

MORPETH & HOUGHTON-LE-SPRING

26	R. Binkes	9687(6-12)	1 ret. jny. Tu./Wed.
26	R. March	9697(4 —)	1 ret. jny. Tu./Wed.

MORPETH & NORTH SHIELDS

16	W. Dunn	9847(6-12)	1 ret. jny. Tu./Wed.

MORPETH & OTTERBURN

22	R. Anderson	9838(4-8)	1 ret. jny. Tu./Wed.

MORPETH & WOOLER

31	W. Fairmington	9977(4-8)	1 ret. jny. Tu./Wed.

NEWARK & GRANTHAM

14	W. Moore & Co.	7893 (4-5)	1 ret. jny. Mon. to Sat.

NEWARK & MANSFIELD

20	J. Gilstrap & Co.	7910(4-8)	1 ret. jny. daily

NEWARK & RETFORD

20	W. Clay	7916(4 —)	1 ret. jny. Mon. to Sat.

NEWBURY & HUNGERFORD

8½	R. Palmer	7229 (4-2)	1 ret. jny. Tu., Th., Sat.

NEWCASTLE-UNDER-LYME & UTTOXETER

18	J. Tranter	8074(9 —)	1 ret. jny. Tu., Th., Sat.

NEWCASTLE UPON TYNE & ALNWICK
33	G. Caxon & Co.	9972 (4-8) 1 ret. jny. Mon. to Sat.
34	L. Pauling & Co.	9839, 9840 (4-11) 1 ret. jny. daily

NEWCASTLE UPON TYNE & BARNARD CASTLE
40	J. Radford & Co.	9829 (4-8) 1 ret. jny. Tu. to Sat., 1 sgl. jny. Sun. & Mon.

NEWCASTLE UPON TYNE & BEDLINGTON
12	W. Darling & Co.	9874 (4-11) 1 ret. jny. Wed. & Sat.

NEWCASTLE UPON TYNE & BERWICK
62	T. Lough & Co.	9824, 9825 (4-8) 1 ret. jny. Mon. to Sat.

NEWCASTLE UPON TYNE & BLAYDON
4	B. Dryden & Co.	9849 (6-12) 4 ret. jnys. Mon. to Sat., 1 ret. jny. Sun.
4	J. Matthewson	9713 (4-14) 2 ret. jnys. daily
4	J. Hemdaugh	9818 (6-12) 4 ret. jnys. Mon. to Fri., 6 ret. jnys. Sat., 2 ret. jnys. Sun.

NEWCASTLE UPON TYNE & BLYTHE
16	T. Reanly	9822 (6-12) 1 ret. jny. Tu. & Sat.

NEWCASTLE UPON TYNE & CARLISLE
40	J. Radford & Co.	9622, 9830 (4-11) 1 ret. jny. daily

(passengers travel by train between Blaydon and Hexham)

NEWCASTLE UPON TYNE & DURHAM
15	J. Thwaites	9681 (6-12) 1 ret. jny. Mon. to Sat.

NEWCASTLE UPON TYNE & EDINBURGH
119	J. Radford & Co.	9722 (4-8) 1 ret. jny. Mon. to Sat.
102	J. Radford & Co.	9805 (4-8) 1 ret. jny. Mon. to Sat.
112	J. Radford & Co.	9809 (4-8) 1 ret. jny. Mon. to Sat.

NEWCASTLE UPON TYNE & HOUGHTON-LE-SPRING
12	R. Binkes	9687 (6-12) 1 ret. jny. Sat. only

NEWCASTLE UPON TYNE & LEEDS
92	W. Atkinson & Co.	8814, 8817 (4-8) 1 ret. jny. Mon. to Sat.
95	M. Outhwaite & Co.	8404 (4-11) 1 sgl. jny. daily
96	M. Outhwaite & Co.	8410 (4-8) 1 sgl. jny. Mon. to Sat.
93	M. Outhwaite & Co.	8403 (4-11) 1 sgl. jny. Mon. to Sat.
92	J. Hemshaugh & Co.	9856 (4-8) 1 sgl. jny. Mon. to Sat.
96	T. Lough & Co.	9728 (4-8) 1 sgl. jny. Mon. to Sat.
95	J. Radford & Co.	9832 (4-11) 1 sgl. jny. daily
93	J. Radford & Co.	9833 (4-11) 1 sgl. jny. Mon. to Sat.

NEWCASTLE UPON TYNE & MIDDLETON
39	T. Lough & Co.	9858 (4-8) 1 ret. jny. Mon. to Sat.

NEWCASTLE UPON TYNE & MORPETH
14	A. Johnson	9707 (6-12) 1 ret. jny. Wed. only
14	A. Dixon & Co.	9816 (6-12) 1 ret. jny. Wed. only

NEWCASTLE UPON TYNE & NORTH SHIELDS			
7½	J. Wilson	9863 (4—)	3 ret. jnys. daily
7½	A. Watson	9869 (4—)	3 ret. jnys. daily
7½	A. Brown & Co.	9853 (4-2)	3 ret. jnys. daily
7½	A. Brown & Co.	9807 (4—)	3 ret. jnys. daily
7½	A. Brown & Co.	9802 (4-2)	3 ret. jnys. daily
7½	J. Wilson	9803 (4—)	3 ret. jnys. daily
7½	J. Wilson	9804 (4—)	3 ret. jnys. daily
7½	J. Wilson	9806 (4—)	3 ret. jnys. daily
7½	J. Wilson	9801 (6—)	3 ret. jnys. daily
7½	A. Watson	9800 (4—)	3 ret. jnys. daily
7½	R. Hall	9815 (4—)	3 ret. jnys. daily
7½	J. Bezelley	9823 (5-1)	3 ret. jnys. daily
NEWCASTLE UPON TYNE & SUNDERLAND			
12	T. Lough & Co.	9879 (4-8)	3 ret. jnys. Mon. to Sat., 2 ret. jnys. Sun.
12	J. Radford & Co.	9878 (4-8)	3 ret. jnys. Mon. to Sat., 2 ret. jnys. Sun.
12	J. Brown & Co.	9857 (4-11)	1 ret. jny. daily
12	J. Hendhaugh & Co.	9134 (4-8)	4 ret. jnys. daily
12	A. Dixon & Co.	9845 (6-12)	2 ret. jnys. Mon. to Sat., 1 ret. jny. Sun.
NEWCASTLE UPON TYNE & TYNEMOUTH			
8	E. Reid	9860 (6—)	4 ret. jnys. daily
8	E. Reid	9696 (6—)	4 ret. jnys. daily
8	E. Reid	9699 (6—)	4 ret. jnys. daily
8	E. Reid	9714 (6—)	4 ret. jnys. daily
8	E. Reid	9820 (6—)	4 ret. jnys. daily
8	A. Johnson	9813 (6-12)	1 ret. jny. daily
8	W. Dunn	9812 (8-7)	1 ret. jny. Mon. to Sat.
8	W. Dunn	9811 (6-12)	1 ret. jny. daily
8	W. Dunn	9810 (4—)	3 ret. jnys. daily
NEWCASTLE UPON TYNE & YORK			
81	J. Radford & Co.	8737, 9827 (4-11)	1 ret. jny. daily
81	J. Radford & Co.	8728, 9828 (4-8)	1 ret. jny. daily
NEWPORT Hants & COWES			
5	Mewitt & Co.	6075 (4-8)	2 ret. jnys. daily
NEWPORT Hants & RYDE			
7½	R. Yelf	6078 (4-10)	1 ret. jny. daily
7½	B. Tice & Co.	6056 (4-5)	1 ret. jny. daily
NEWPORT Mon & PONTYPOOL			
11	J. Rowberry	7702 (4-8)	1 ret. jny. Mon. to Sat.
NORTHAMPTON & CHELTENHAM			
69	T. Haines & Co.	7422 (4-5)	1 sgl. jny. Mon. to Sat.

NORTHAMPTON & DAVENTRY
12 W. Goodman & Co.   6927(4-2) 1 ret. jny. Mon., Tu., Th., Sat.

NORTHAMPTON & STAMFORD
36 F. Mulliner & Co.   6916(4-5) 1 ret. jny. Tu., Th., Sat.

NORTHAMPTON & WELLINGBOROUGH
10 J. Sears   6924(6-3) 1 ret. jny. Tu., Th., Sat.

NORTH SHIELDS & BLYTH
10 T. Readley   9821(6-6) 1 ret. jny. Mon. to Sat.

NORTHWICH & RUNCORN
11½ W. Partington & Co.   8224(4-8) 1 ret. jny. daily

NORWICH & BURY ST. EDMUNDS
41 C. Thorpe & Co.   6661(4-8) 1 ret. jny. Mon., Wed., Sat.

NORWICH & CROMER
22 T. Purley   6751(2-4) 1 ret. jny. daily
22 C. Gee & Co.   6756(4-5) 1 ret. jny. daily

NORWICH & EAST DEREHAM
16 C. Catton   6763(2-7) 1 ret. jny. Mon., Wed., Sat.

NORWICH & HALESWORTH
23 W. Hammond & Co.   6701(4-8) 1 ret. jny. Mon. to Sat.

NORWICH & HARLESTON
19 R. Keen   6754(4-5) 1 ret. jny. Wed. & Sat.

NORWICH & HOLT
24 W. Tuck   6762(— 4) 3 sgl. jnys. Th./Fri.
24 W. Tuck   6761(4-8) 1 ret. jny. Mon., Wed., Sat.

NORWICH & LITCHAM
24 J. Botts & Co.   6759(6—) 1 ret. jny. Sat. only

NORWICH & LOWESTOFT
27½ C. Ansdell & Co.   6702(4-8) 1 ret. jny. Mon., Wed., Sat.

NORWICH & LYNN
44 W. Durrant & Co.   6755(4-8) 1 ret. jny. Mon. to Sat.

NORWICH & NEWARK
116 J. Wiggins & Co.   6753(4-11) 1 sgl. jny. Mon. to Sat.
116 J. Gilstrap & Co.   7923(4-11) 1 sgl. jny. Mon. to Sat.

NORWICH & NORTH WALSHAM
14 R. Scott   6769(4 —) 1 ret. jny. Tu., Th., Sat.
14 T. Bensley   6768(4 —) 1 ret. jny. Tu., Th., Sat., Sun.
14 W. Cooper   6758(6-3) 1 ret. jny. Mon., Wed., Fri., Sun.

NORWICH & STRADBROKE
26 R. Keen & Co.   6754(4-5) 1 ret. jny. Mon., Wed., Sat.

NORWICH & WATTON
21 R. Coe   6764(4-8) 1 ret. jny. Sat. only

NORWICH & WELLS
35 J. Ward   6760 (4-5) I ret. jny. Wed. & Sat.

NORWICH & YARMOUTH
22½ D. Hogarth & Co. 6730 (4-5) I ret. jny. daily
22½ D. Hogarth & Co. 6731 (4-8) I ret. jny. Mon., Tu., Th., Fri.
20 D. Hogarth & Co. 6731 (4-8) I ret. jny. Wed. & Sat.

NOTTINGHAM & BARTON-UPON-HUMBER
71 T. Walkden & Co. 7854 (4-11) I sgl. jny. Mon. to Sat.
73 J. Simpson & Co. 7895 (4-11) I sgl. jny. Mon. to Sat.

NOTTINGHAM & BELPER
16 J. Webster   7995 (6-9) I ret. jny. Mon., Th., Sat.

NOTTINGHAM & BROUGHTON
12 J. Hemsley   7919 (9—) I ret. jny. Wed. & Sat.

NOTTINGHAM & DERBY
16 J. Hardy & Co.   7926 (4-8) I ret. jny. Mon. to Sat.
16 J. Wilmot & Co.   7927 (4-11) I ret. jny. Mon. to Sat.
16 J. Wilmot & Co.   7903 (4-11) I ret. jny. daily
16 J. Wilmot & Co.   7896 (4-11) I ret. jny. Mon. to Sat.
16 J. Simpson & Co. 7890 (4-11) I ret. jny. daily

NOTTINGHAM & DONCASTER
42 J. Wilmot & Co.   7907 (4-8) I ret. jny. Mon. to Sat.
42 W. Wright   7908 (4-5) I sgl. jny. Mon. to Sat.

NOTTINGHAM & HEANOR
10 R. C. Grammer   7992 (4-8) I ret. jny. Mon., Wed., Fri., Sat.

NOTTINGHAM & ILKESTON
8 R. Burrows   8008 (4—) I ret. jny. Mon., Wed., Sat.

NOTTINGHAM & LEICESTER
26 J. Wilmot & Co,   7901 (4-11) I ret. jny. daily
26 J. Wilmot & Co,   7930 (4-8) I ret. jny. Mon. to Sat.
26 J. Simpson & Co. 7906 (4-11) I ret. jny. Mon. to Sat.
26 C. S. Pettifor & Co. 6963 (4-11) I ret. jny. daily

NOTTINGHAM & LINCOLN
37 J. Wilmot & Co.   7899 (4-11) I ret. jny. daily
37 J. Hardy & Co.   7932 (4-8) I ret. jny. Mon. to Sat. only
37 J. Hardy & Co.   7933 (4-11) I ret. jny. daily

NOTTINGHAM & LOUGHBOROUGH
15 J. Shepherd & Co. 6955 (7-2) I ret. jny. Tu., Wed., Fri., Sun.

NOTTINGHAM & MANSFIELD
14 S. Miller & Co.   7913 (—9) I ret. jny. Mon. to Sat.

NOTTINGHAM & NEWARK
| 21 | J. Wilmot & Co. | 7898(4-11) | ret. jny. daily |
| 20 | J. Simpson & Co. | 7897(4-11) | ret. jny. Mon. to Sat. |

NOTTINGHAM & STAMFORD
| 45 | J. Hardy & Co. | 7909(4-5) | ret. jny. Mon. to Sat. |

NOTTINGHAM & SUTTON IN ASHFIELD
| 14 | T. Bullock | 7917(9—) | ret. jny. Wed. & Sat. |
| 14 | W. Radford & Co. | 7905(6—) | ret. jny. Mon., Wed., Sat. |

OLNEY & WOBURN
| 23 | J. Gilbert | 6860(4-5) | sgl. jny. Mon. to Sat. |

OUNDLE & KINGS CLIFFE
| 7 | J. Lotan | 6922(4—) | sgl. jny. Mon. to Sat. |

OXFORD & ABINGDON
| 6 | A. Sheller | 7227(4-2) | ret. jny. Mon. to Sat. |

OXFORD & BATH
63	R. Costar & Co.	7205(4-5)	sgl. jny. Mon. to Sat.
70	R. Costar & Co.	7206,7210(4-5)	ret. jny. Mon. to Sat.
62	W. Lane & Co.	5844(4-5)	sgl. jny. Mon. to Sat.

OXFORD & CAMBRIDGE
| 87 | R. Costar & Co. | 7204(4-5) | sgl. jny. Mon. to Sat. |

OXFORD & NORTHAMPTON
| 40 | J. Neyler & Co. | 7383(4-5) | ret. jny. daily |
| 43 | R. Costar & Co. | 6928(4-5) | ret. jny. daily |

OXFORD & READING
| 28 | R. Costar & Co. | 7208(4-8) | ret. jny. daily |
| 28 | R. Costar & Co. | 7209(4-5) | ret. jny. daily |

OXFORD & SOUTHAMPTON
| 64 | W. Curtis & Co. | 6068,6072(4-11) | ret. jny. Mon. to Sat. |
| 62 | W. Spurrier & Co. | 6083(4-5) | sgl. jny. Mon. to Sat. |

OXFORD & STOW-ON-THE-WOLD
| 27 | R. Costar & Co. | 7228(4-5) | ret. jny. daily |

OXFORD & WARWICK
| 47 | J. Drinkwater | 7200,7201(4-8) | ret. jny. Mon. to Sat. |

PENRITH & HEXHAM
| 41 | A. Charlton | 9837(4-8) | sgl. jny. Mon. to Sat. |

PENZANCE & TRURO
26	W. Pearce & Co.	5500(14-1)	ret. jny. Mon. to Sat.
26	W. Stephens & Co.	5502(4-8)	sgl. jny. daily
26	J. Cockram & Co.	5503(4-5)	sgl. jny. daily

PETERBOROUGH & ST. IVES
| 24 | D. Household & Co. | 6863(4-5) | ret. jny. daily |

PETERBOROUGH & STILTON		
6	G. Clifton	6910 (4-5) 1 ret. jny. Mon. to Sat.
PLYMOUTH & BARNSTAPLE		
63	W. Rowe & Co.	5660 (4-8) 1 ret. jny. Mon. to Sat. (65 miles Tu., Th., Sat.
PLYMOUTH & DEVONPORT		
2	W. Radmore & Co.	5661, 5662 (12—) 24 ret. jnys. Mon. to Sat.
PLYMOUTH & KINGSBRIDGE		
20	R. Foall	5637 (4-11) 1 sgl. jny. Mon. to Sat.
20	W. Rowe & Co.	5663 (4-8) 1 sgl. jny. Mon. to Sat.
PONTEFRACT & KNOTTINGLEY		
3	J. Hill	8441 (6—) 1 ret. jny. Mon. to Sat.
PORTSMOUTH & CHICHESTER		
36	T. Stones & Co.	6172 (4-8) 1 sgl. jny. Mon. to Sat.
PORTSMOUTH & READING		
52	W. Hone & Co.	7225 (4-5) 1 sgl. jny. Mon. to Sat.
PRESTON & BLACKBURN		
9½	J. Briggs	9446 (4—) 1 ret. jny. Sat. only
11	G. Cotton	8960 (4-8) 1 ret. jny. Wed. only
11	R. Cooke	8964 (4-8) 1 ret. jny. Wed. only
11	J. Croft & Co.	8966 (4—) 1 ret. jny. alt. Sat.
PRESTON & BLACKPOOL		
18	J. Bamper & Co.	8941 (4—) 1 ret. jny. alt. Sat.
18	R. Carter	8958 (4—) 1 ret. jny. Sat. only
21	E. Clough & Co.	8961 (4-8) 1 ret. jny. Mon. to Sat.
18	T. Fisher & Co.	8983 (4-5) 1 ret. jny. Mon., Wed., Sat.
22	J. Hardman & Co.	9017 (4-8) 1 ret. jny. Mon. to Sat.
PRESTON & CHIPPING		
11	J. Lund & Co.	9438 (6-6) 1 ret. jny. Sat. only
PRESTON & KIRKHAM		
9	R. Lund	9049 (4—) 1 ret. jny. Wed. & Sat.
PRESTON & WIGAN		
18	W. Sleddon	9409 (4-11) 1 ret. jny. Sat. only
18	J. Croft & Co.	9129 (4-5) 1 ret. jny. Mon. to Sat.
PUCKERIDGE & WARE		
6	R. Fagg & Co.	10003 (4-5) 1 ret. jny. Mon. to Sat.
RAMSGATE & DEAL		
13	J. Smith	6287 (5-1) 1 ret. jny. daily
READING & BASINGSTOKE		
16	W. Lodder	7222 (4—) 1 ret. jny. daily

READING & HENLEY

8	T. Bowling	7214(4 —)	1 ret. jny. Mon. to Sat.
9	T. Bowling	7242(4 —)	1 ret. jny. Wed. & Sat.
8	N. Thorn	7216(3 - 1)	1 ret. jny. Mon. to Sat.

READING & NEWBURY

| 17 | S. Elkins | 7218(6 —) | 1 ret. jny. Mon. to Sat. |
| 17 | W.C. Lay | 7217(6 —) | 1 ret. jny. Mon. to Sat. |

READING & WALLINGFORD

| 16 | W. Hone | 7220(4 —) | 1 ret. jny. Mon. to Sat. |

READING & WINDSOR

| 20 | W. Pook | 7219(2 - 4) | 1 ret. jny. Mon. to Sat. |
| 20 | T. Bunce | 7232(4 - 2) | 1 ret. jny. Mon. to Sat. |

RETFORD & WORKSOP

| 8 | G. Spray | 7923(4 —) | 1 ret. jny. Mon. to Sat. |
| 8 | J. Richardson | 7902(4 —) | 1 ret. jny. daily |

RICHMOND & HIGH STREET (Yorks.)

| 4 | J. Wilson | 8678(— 6) | 2 ret. jnys. Mon. to Sat. |

RICKMANSWORTH & WATFORD

| 3 | W. Wyatt & Co. | 10007(2 - 4) | 1 ret. jny. daily |

RIPON & HARROGATE

| 11 | T. Pearson & Co. | 8870(4 - 5) | 1 ret. jny. daily |

RIPON & RICHMOND

| 24 | J. Francis & Co. | 8883(4 - 5) | 1 sgl. jny. Mon. to Sat. |

ROCHDALE & BACUP

| 7 | T. Horrocks & Co. | 9025(4 - 8) | 1 ret. jny. Mon. only |

ROCHDALE & BOLTON

| 11 | T. Howarth | 9011 (4 - 5) | 2 ret. jnys. Mon. to Sat., 1 ret. jny. Sun. |

ROCHDALE & BURY

| 7 | T. Hall | 9024(4 - 8) | 1 ret. jny. Mon. only |
| 7 | E. Wilding | 9125 (4 - 8) | 1 ret. jny. Mon. only |

ROCHDALE & HASLINGDEN

| 10½ | W. Boyd | 9468(— 6) | 1 ret. jny. Wed. only |

ROCHDALE & HEBDEN BRIDGE

| 13 | T. Baldwin & Co. | 8816 (4 - 11) | 1 ret. jny. Mon. only |

ROCHDALE & HEYWOOD

| 3 | T. Battersby | 8908 (4 - 11) | 1 ret. jny. Mon. only |
| 3 | J. Hope | 9023(6 - 3) | 1 ret. jny. Mon. only |

ROCHDALE & NEW CHURCH

| 8 | J. Chadwick | 8957(4 - 8) | 1 ret. jny. Mon. only |

ROCHDALE & OLDHAM
| 5 | J. Grindrod | 9002 (4-2) | 1 ret. jny. Mon. only |
| 5 | J. Buckley & Co. | 8939 (6-9) | 1 ret. jny. Mon. only |

ROCHDALE & SHAW
| 4 | R. Mellor | 9060 (4-8) | 1 ret. jny. Mon. only |

ROCHDALE & WHITWORTH
| 3 | J. Lomax | 9051 (4-8) | 1 ret. jny. Mon. only |

ROCHESTER & SITTINGBOURNE
| 11 | B. Peters | 6298 (5-1) | 1 ret. jny. Mon. to Sat. |
| 11 | B. Peters | 6494 (4—) | 1 ret. jny. Mon. to Sat. |

RUGBY & DAVENTRY
| 10 | W. Smith & Co. | 10037 (4-5) | 1 sgl. jny. Mon. to Sat. |

RUTHIN & MOLD
| 10 | J. Smart & Co. | 8357 (9 —) | 1 ret. jny. Mon. to Sat. |

SAFFRON WALDEN & BISHOPS STORTFORD
| 12 | H. Gilby & Co. | 6886 (4-8) | 1 ret. jny. Tu. to Sat. |

SALISBURY & FROME
| 28 | J. Smith | 5924 (6 —) | 1 ret. jny. Mon./Tu. |

SALISBURY & POOLE
| 37 | W. Philpott & Co. | 6005 (4-5) | 1 sgl. jny. Mon. to Sat. |

SALISBURY & SOUTHAMPTON
| 23 | J. Cocks | 6004 (3-6) | 1 ret. jny. Mon. to Sat. (22 miles on Tu., Th., Sat.) |

SANDHURST & HECKFIELD
| 8 | J. Monk | 7212 (4-5) | 1 ret. jny. Mon. to Sat. |

SCARBOROUGH & FLASK (Fylingdale)
| 12 | J. Hammond & Co. | 8875 (4-8) | 1 ret. jny. Mon. to Sat. |

SHEFFIELD & BARLBOROUGH
| 10 | J. Brown | 8628 (4-8) | 1 ret. jny. Tu. & Sat. |

SHEFFIELD & BUXTON
| 28 | W.L. Bickley & Co. | 8651 (4-8) | 1 ret. jny. Mon. to Sat. |

SHEFFIELD & CHESTERFIELD
| 12 | W. Hopkinson | 7991 (4-11) | 1 ret. jny. Mon. to Sat. |

SHEFFIELD & DONCASTER
18	W. Hutchinson & Co.	8653 (4-11)	1 ret. jny. Sun. only
18	W. Bradley & Co.	8612, 8622 (4-8)	2 ret. jnys. daily
18	W.L. Bickley & Co.	8620, 8621 (4-8)	2 ret. jnys. daily

SHEFFIELD & ECKINGTON
| 6 | R. Fletcher | 8000 (4-11) | 1 ret. jny. Tu. & Sat. |

SHEFFIELD & LEEDS
| 33 | T. Percival & Co. | 8443 (4-8) | 1 ret. jny. Mon. to Sat. |
| 33 | W.L. Bickley & Co. | 8656 (4-8) | 1 ret. jny. Mon. to Sat. |

SHEFFIELD & LINCOLN
50 W. Bradley & Co.   8638 (4-8) 1 ret. jny. Mon. to Sat.

SHEFFIELD & NEWBRIDGE
32 W. Hutchinson & Co. 8653 (4-11) 1 ret. jny. Mon. to Sat.
32 W.L. Bickley & Co. 8590 (4-8) 1 ret. jny. Mon. to Sat.
32 W.L. Bickley & Co. 8606 (4-11) 1 ret. jny. Mon. to Sat.

SHEFFIELD & RETFORD
26 G. Spray   8610 (4-8) 1 ret. jny. Mon. to Sat.

SHEFFIELD & ROTHERHAM
6   T. Percival   8607 (4-11) 1 ret. jny. Mon. & Sun.
6   T. Clifford   8649 (4-8) 2 ret. jnys. daily
6   T. Percival   8608 (6 —) 1 ret. jny. daily
6   T. Percival   8594 (4-8) 2 ret. jnys. daily
6   R. Marshall   8633 (6 —) 1 ret. jny. Tu. only
6   T. Pinder   8601 (5-1) 1 ret. jny. Sun. only

SHEFFIELD & WORKSOP
18   T. Pinder   8602 (4-5) 1 ret. jny. Mon., Wed., Fri., Sun.

SHREWSBURY & ABERYSTWYTH
75 J. Jobson & Co. 8153 (4-5) 1 ret. jny. Mon./Tu., Th./Fri.
77 J. Taylor & Co.   8149 (4-8) 1 sgl. jny. Tu. & Sat.
75 J. Taylor & Co.   8148 (4-8) 1 sgl. jny. Mon. & Fri.
75 A.B. Davies & Co. 7796 (4-11) 1 sgl. jny. Mon. & Fri.
75 E. Evans & Co.   7800 (4-11) 1 sgl. jny. Tu. & Sat.

SHREWSBURY & BANGOR
83 J. Taylor & Co.   8160, 8168 (4-8) 1 ret. jny. daily

SHREWSBURY & CHESTER
40 J. Jones & Co.   8244 (4-8) 1 ret. jny. Mon. to Sat.

SHREWSBURY & HANLEY
44 H.J. Taylor & Co. 8155 (4-5) 1 ret. jny. Mon. to Sat.

SHREWSBURY & HEREFORD
53 H.J. Taylor & Co. 7638, 8167 (4-5) 1 ret. jny. Mon. to Sat.

SHREWSBURY & HOLYHEAD
108 J. Jobson & Co. 8156, 8162, 8164 (4-5) 1 ret. jny. Mon. to Sat.

SHREWSBURY & MONTGOMERY
21 E. Read   8359 (4-8) 1 ret. jny. Sat.

SHREWSBURY & NEWCASTLE-UNDER-LYME
33 T. Sandalls & Co. 8170 (4 —) 1 ret. jny. Mon./Tu., Fri./Sat.

SHREWSBURY & NEWTOWN
32 J. Taylor & Co.   8358 (4-4) 1 ret. jny. daily

SHREWSBURY & OSWESTRY
18 J. Jenkins   8151 (4-5) 1 ret. jny. Mon. to Sat.

SHREWSBURY & ROCK FERRY		
52	J. Jobson & Co.	8165(4-8) 1 ret. jny. daily
SITTINGBOURNE & SHEERNESS		
10	F. Pratten	6295(4—) 1 ret. jny. Mon. to Sat.
SOUTHAMPTON & CHELTENHAM		
89	W. Curtis & Co.	6055(4-8) 1 sgl. jny. Mon. to Sat.
89	W. Halcomb & Co.	6062(4-8) 1 sgl. jny. Mon. to Sat.
SOUTHAMPTON & CHRISTCHURCH		
30	W. Curtis & Co.	6080(4-5) 1 ret. jny. Mon. to Sat.
SOUTHAMPTON & GOSPORT		
16	H. Shilton	6051 (3-6) 1 ret. jny. Mon. to Sat.
SOUTHAMPTON & LYMINGTON		
18	W. Spurrier	6066 (3-3) 1 ret. jny. daily
18	W. Curtis & Co.	6067 (4-2) 1 ret. jny. daily
SOUTHAMPTON & POOLE		
36	T. Hyde	5975(4-5) 1 ret. jny. Mon. to Sat.
SOUTHAMPTON & READING		
46	W. Hicks & Co.	7213 (4-5) 1 sgl. jny. Mon. to Sat.
50	T. Burden & Co.	6085(4-5) 1 sgl. jny. Mon. to Sat.
SOUTHAMPTON & TAUNTON		
92	E. Whitmarsh & Co.	5933(4-5) 1 sgl. jny. Mon. to Sat.
SOUTHAMPTON & WEYMOUTH		
76	W. Curtis & Co.	6070, 6071(4-5) 1 ret. jny. Mon. to Sat.
69	W. Spurrier & Co.	6064, 6065(4-5) 1 ret. jny. Mon. to Sat.
SOUTHAMPTON & WINCHESTER		
12	H. Mason & Co.	6074 (4-5) 1 ret. jny. Mon. to Sat.
12	W. Spurrier & Co.	6059(3-3) 1 ret. jny. Mon. to Sat.
SOUTHPORT & SCARISBRIC BRIDGE		
6	J. Salthouse	7429 (6-6) 1 ret. jny. Tu., Fri., Sat.
6	J. Halfey	9431(6-6) 1 ret. jny. Mon., Wed., Th.
SOUTH SHIELDS & MONKWEARMOUTH		
6	T. B. Oyston & Co.	9688, 9689, 9690, 9691 (4-2) 28 ret. jnys. daily
SPALDING & HOLBEACH		
8	J. Rainey	7840 (—3) 1 ret. jny. Mon. to Sat.
STAFFORD & NEWPORT		
12	H. J. Taylor & Co.	8150 (4-5) 1 ret. jny. Tu., Th., Sat.
STAMFORD & MELTON MOWBRAY		
21	J. Standwell & Co.	7839(4-5) 1 ret. jny. daily
STAMFORD & NEWARK		
35	J. Standwell & Co.	7836 (4-5) 1 ret. jny. Mon. to Sat.

STANHOPE & GATESHEAD
28 W.T. Greenwell & Co. 9711 (6-6) 1 sgl. jny. Mon. to Sat.

ST. HELENS & SOUTHPORT
21 B. Bretherton & Co. 9443 (4-8) 1 ret. jny. Mon. to Sat.
21 E. Fuller 9462 (4-8) 1 ret. jny. Mon. to Sat.

ST. IVES & RAMSEY (Hunts.)
9 S. Beard 6865 (6—) 1 ret. jny. Mon. only
9 J. Cox 6864 (6—) 1 ret. jny. Mon. only

STOCKPORT & DUKINFIELD
7 J. Drury 8973 (4-8) 1 ret. jny. Fri. only

STOCKPORT & HAYFIELD
11 R. Quarmby 7996 (4-8) 1 ret. jny. Fri. only

STOCKPORT & MELLOR
6 W. Hanney 8007 (6—) 1 ret. jny. Fri. only

STOCKPORT & NEW MILLS
8 J. Bradbury & Co. 7998 (4-11) 1 ret. jny. Fri. only

STOCKTON & FLASK (Fylingdale)
43 W. Ludley & Co. 9702 (4-8) 1 sgl. jny. Mon. to Sat.
43 M. Yeoman & Co. 8885 (4-8) 1 ret. jny. Mon. to Sat.

STOCKTON & HARTLEPOOL
12 J. Brown & Co. 9701 (4-8) 1 ret. jny. Mon., Wed., Sat.

STOWMARKET & IPSWICH
12 J. Nelson & Co. 10040 (4-2) 1 ret. jny. daily

STRATFORD-UPON-AVON & CHIPPING CAMPDEN
12 T. Ellis 7580 (4-5) 1 ret. jny. Fri. only

STROUD & CLAYPITS
6 J.E. Wakefield & Co. 7404 (2-4) 1 ret. jny. Mon. to Sat.

STROUD & TETBURY
10 R. Parker & Co. 7388 (4-8) 1 ret. jny. Tu., Th., Fri.

SUNDERLAND & CHESTER-LE-STREET
9 W. Halliday & Co. 9876 (4—) 1 ret. jny. Mon. only

SUNDERLAND & MONKWEARMOUTH
1 T.B. Ayston & Co. 9692 (4-2) 2 ret. jnys. daily

SUNDERLAND & MORPETH
26 S. Brown 9880 (6-2) 1 ret. jny. Tu./Wed.

SUNDERLAND & SEAHAM
7 J. Davison 9723 (5-1) 2 ret. jnys. Mon. to Sat., 1 ret.
jny. Sat.

SUNDERLAND & STOCKTON
28 W. Ludley & Co. 9706 (4-8) 1 ret. jny. Mon. to Sat.

TAPLOW & MARLOW
7 W. Tollitt 10018 (4-2) 1 ret. jny. Mon. to Sat.

TAUNTON & BARNSTAPLE
51 H. Whitmarsh & Co.   5926, 5928 (4-8) I ret. jny. Mon. to Sat.

TAUNTON & BRIDGWATER
11 A. Mellard   3920 (4-2) I ret. jny. Mon. to Sat.

TAUNTON & SIDMOUTH
26 H. Whitmarsh & Co.   5925 (4-5) I ret. jny. Mon. to Sat.

TAUNTON & WIVELISCOMBE
10 E. Cattle   5922 (4-2) I ret. jny. Mon., Wed., Sat.
10 J. Featherstone & Co.   5923 (4-5) I ret. jny. Mon., Wed., Sat.

TROWBRIDGE & BRADFORD-ON-AVON
3 W. Winsor   6014 (12-3) 2 ret. jnys. Mon. to Sat.

TRURO & TORPOINT
50 W. Kellow   5501, 5505 (6 —) I ret. jny. Mon. to Sat.

UPMINSTER & ROMFORD
4 E. Deacon   10033 (4-2) I ret. jny. Sat. only

WAKEFIELD & BRIGHOUSE
12 S. Waddington   8795 (4-8) I ret. jny. Fri. only

WAKEFIELD & DEWSBURY
6 T. Wormald   8826 (4-11) I ret. jny. Fri. only

WAKEFIELD & DONCASTER
20 A. Lockwood & Co.   8819 (4-8) I ret. jny. Mon. to Sat.

WAKEFIELD & PONTEFRACT
9 T. Dunnil   8799 (4-5) I ret. jny. Sat. only

WAKEFIELD & TODMORDEN
27 T. Baldwin & Co.   8815 (4-11) I ret. jny. Fri. only

WANTAGE & HIGHWORTH
16   7234 (2-4) I ret. jny. Mon. to Sat.

WARRINGTON & LEIGH
10 M. A. Kirkman   9435 (4-11) I ret. jny. Wed. only

WARWICK & HENLEY-IN-ARDEN
9 W. Johns & Co.   7069 (4-11) I ret. jny. Sat. only

WATLINGTON & WEST WYCOMBE
11 W. Taplin   7226 (2-4) I sgl. jny. Mon. to Sat.

WELSHPOOL & BIRKENHEAD
58 J. Poole & Co.   8202 (4-12) I sgl. jny. Mon. to Sat.

WELWYN & BALDOCK
12 J. Kershaw   6881 (4-5) I ret. jny. Mon. to Sat.

WENDOVER & UXBRIDGE
20 W. Tollitt   10010 (4-11) I ret. jny. Mon. to Sat.

WEST DRAYTON & UXBRIDGE
3 R. Green   10034 (4-2) I ret. jny. Mon. to Sat.

WHITEHAVEN & COCKERMOUTH			
14	A.J.Kinley	9613(4—)	I ret. jny. Mon. only
WHITEHAVEN & EGREMONT			
6	A.J.Kinley	9613(4—)	I ret. jny. Sat. only
WHITEHAVEN & KENDAL			
59	J.Jackson & Co.	9629,9630(4-8)	I ret. jny. Mon. to Sat.
WHITEHAVEN & MARYPORT			
14	J.Clarke	9616(6—)	I ret. jny. Mon., Th., Sat.
WHITEHAVEN & ULVERSTON			
42	S.Benson	9612(4—)	I ret. jny. Tu./Wed., Fri./Sat.
WHITEHAVEN & WORKINGTON			
8	A.J.Kinley	9613(4—)	I ret. jny. Tu. only
8	J.Gill	9611(4—)	I ret. jny. Tu., Th., Sat.
WHITWELL & CODICOTE			
3	J.Kershaw	6880(4—)	I ret. jny. Mon. to Sat.
WINCHESTER & ROMSEY			
11	A.Collyer & Co.	6057(3-3)	I ret. jny. Mon. to Sat.
WINCHCOMB & TEWKESBURY			
11	W.Tustin	7431(5-4)	I ret. jny. Wed. only
WISBECH & LONG SUTTON			
9	D.Grimsteed	7831(4—)	I ret. jny. Mon. to Sat.
WOLVERHAMPTON & BILSTON			
2½	J.Best	7068(4-8)	
WOLVERHAMPTON & BRIDGNORTH			
14	M.Hall	8157(4-5)	I ret. jny. daily
WOLVERHAMPTON & LICHFIELD			
16	J.Webb & Co.	8089(4-8)	I ret. jny. Mon. to Sat.
WORCESTER & ALCESTER			
17	T.Butler	7584(4-5)	I ret. jny. Sat. only
WORCESTER & BEWDLEY			
14	J.Lewis	7517(4-8)	I sgl. jny. Mon. to Sat.
WORCESTER & BROMSGROVE			
13	J.Blower	7514(8-4)	I ret. jny. Wed. & Sat.
13	T.Albut	7516(8-1)	I ret. jny. Wed. & Sat.
WORCESTER & BROMYARD			
14	M.New	7579(4-11)	I ret. jny. Wed. & Sat.
14	T.Price	7641(4-11)	I ret. jny. Mon., Wed., Sat.
WORCESTER & CARMARTHEN			
113	J.Davies & Co.	7634(4-8)	I sgl. jny. Mon. to Sat.
WORCESTER & CHELTENHAM			
24	J.Jones & Co.	7589(4-8)	I ret. jny. Mon. to Sat.

WORCESTER & EVESHAM		
16	R. Vince	7578 (4-5) I ret. jny. Wed. & Sat.
15	R. Kendrick	7583 (3-1) I ret. jny. Wed. & Sat.
WORCESTER & FLADBURY		
11	W. Curmock	7581 (4-2) I ret. jny. Wed. & Sat.
WORCESTER & HANLEY CASTLE		
5½	T. Baylis	7590 (5-1) I ret. jny. Wed. & Sat.
WORCESTER & HEREFORD		
31	T. Reeves & Co.	7631, 7632 (4-8) I ret. jny. Mon. to Sat.
WORCESTER & HUNDRED HOUSE		
11	T. Bunce	7573 (4-8) I ret. jny. Mon., Wed., Sat.
WORCESTER & KIDDERMINSTER		
14	S. Cole	7523 (7-2) I ret. jny. Mon., Wed., Sat.
14	J. Gardener	7522 (9-3) I ret. jny. Mon., Tu., Wed., Th., Sat.
WORCESTER & LEAMINGTON		
44	J. Jones & Co.	7588 (4-5) I sgl. jny. Mon. to Sat.
WORCESTER & LEOMINSTER		
26	T. Reeves & Co.	7630 (4-5) I ret. jny. Tu., Th., Sat.
WORCESTER & MALVERN		
8	T. Tipping	7585 (4-2) I ret. jny. Mon. to Fri.
WORCESTER & PERSHORE		
9	J. Goore	7575 (4-8) I ret. jny. Mon., Wed., Sat.
WORCESTER & ROSS		
29	J. Barratt	7644 (4-8) I sgl. jny. Mon. to Sat.
WORCESTER & STOURPORT		
11	J. Purser	7521 (6-3) I ret. jny. Mon., Wed., Sat.
WORCESTER & WOLVERHAMPTON		
33	R. Evans & Co.	8090, 8091 (4-8) 2 ret. jnys. daily
WORKSOP & CHESTERFIELD		
16	C. Hubbings	7921 (4 —) I ret. jny. Mon., Wed., Sat.
WRITTLE & CHIPPING ONGAR		
12	J. West & Co.	6595 (2-2) I sgl. jny. Mon. to Sat.
YARMOUTH & BECCLES		
14½	W. Buck	6704 (4 —) I ret. jny. Wed. & Sat.
YARMOUTH & BUNGAY		
21	J. Head	6676 (4 —) I ret. jny. Mon., Wed., Sat.
20	E. Killington	6690 (4 —) I ret. jny. Wed. & Sat.
YARMOUTH & BURY ST. EDMUNDS		
58	D. Hogarth & Co.	6734, 6735 (4-5) I ret. jny. Mon. to Sat.
YARMOUTH & IPSWICH		
54	J. Nelson & Co.	10050 (4-8) I ret. jny. Mon. to Sat.

YARMOUTH & LOWESTOFT
10	J. Balls	6669, 6691 (6 —) 2 ret. jnys. Mon. to Sat.
10	J. Barton	6692 (6 —) 1 ret. jny. Mon., Th., Sat.

YORK & CARLISLE
111	J. Feather & Co.	9626, 9627 (4-11) 1 sgl. jny. daily

YORK & HARROGATE
21	J. Barber & Co.	8722 (4-5) 1 ret. jny. Mon. to Sat.

YORK & HULL
39	R. Chaffer & Co.	8528 (6-12) 1 ret. jny. Mon. to Sat.

YORK & KIRBYMOORSIDE
29	R. Wilton	8881 (4-8) 1 sgl. jny. Mon. to Sat.

YORK & MIDDLEHAM
43	J. Ricknell & Co.	8733 (4-11) 1 sgl. jny. Mon. to Sat.

YORK & SCARBOROUGH
40	J. Barber & Co.	8730 (6-12) 1 ret. jny. Mon. to Sat.

YORK & SELBY
14	G. Firth	8724 (4-8) 1 ret. jny. Mon. to Sat.
14	T. Outhwaite & Co.	8731, 8741 (4-8) 2 ret. jnys. Mon. to Sat.

YORK & SHEFFIELD
53	W. L. Bickley & Co.	8604 (4-8) 1 sgl. jny. Mon. to Sat.
53	R. Cattle & Co.	8723 (4-8) 1 sgl. jny. Mon. to Sat.
51	W. Bradley & Co.	8625, 8742 (4-5) 1 ret. jny. Mon. to Sat.

YORK & WAKEFIELD
29	J. Peart	8734 (—6) 1 ret. jny. Fri. only

YORK & WHITBY
48	J. Barber & Co.	8735 (4-8) 1 ret. jny. Mon., Wed., Fri.

TABLE 4

LOCAL STAGE COACHES

IN THE

LONDON

AREA

SERVICE MILES	PROPRIETOR	COACHES	FREQUENCY
GRACECHURCH STREET & BALHAM HILL			
5	G. Saltwell	1266 (6-6)	4 ret. jnys. daily
5	R. Spooner	1291 (6-9)	5 ret. jnys. daily
5	W. Riches	1295, 1296 (6-9)	8 ret. jnys. daily
5	J. Blackwell	1340 (6-9)	4 ret. jnys. daily
5½	W. Helton	1325, 1367 (6-9)	7 ret. jnys. daily
5½	J. Page	1327 (6-9)	2 ret. jnys. daily
STRAND (Red Lion) & BALHAM HILL			
5½	J. Porter	1326 (6-9)	3 ret. jnys. daily
OXFORD STREET (Green Man & Still) & BALHAM HILL			
5½	J. Blackwell	1342, 1344 (6-6)	8 ret. jnys. daily
CHARING CROSS & BALHAM HILL			
6	W. Sheldrick	1388 (6-6)	3 ret. jnys. daily
PICCADILLY & BANK			
2½	J. Kerrison	23 (14-1)	5 ret. jnys. daily
MITCHAM & BANSTEAD			
8	T. & S. Holden	10015 (4-5)	1 ret. jny. Mon. to Sat.
ALDGATE (The Bull) & BARKING			
7	W. White	5308 (6-9)	2 ret. jnys. daily
LEADENHALL STREET & BATTERSEA			
6½	H. Phillpott	1945, 2249 (12-3)	8 ret. jnys. daily
MILE END GATE & BAYSWATER			
6	G. Moore	26 (13-2)	2 ret. jnys. daily
7	G. Moore	353 (13-2)	3 ret. jnys. daily
6	W. Allcott	175 (14-1)	4 ret. jnys. daily
6	W. Hattersley & Co.	327 (12—)	5 ret. jnys. Mon. to Sat.
CHARING CROSS & BECKENHAM			
10½	W. Inkpen & Co.	1069 (4-8)	3 ret. jnys. daily
GRACECHURCH STREET & BLACKHEATH			
6	C. Collins	437 (6-12)	7 ret. jnys. daily
6¼	J. Driver	429, 430, 431, 432, 433, 434, 435 (6-12) 35 ret. jnys. daily	
STRAND & BLACKHEATH			
7¾	W. Plummer	400 (6-9)	10 ret. jnys. daily
CHARING CROSS & BLACKHEATH			
7¼	W. Plummer	602 (6-9)	10 ret. jnys. daily
8¼	W. Plummer	538 (6-12)	10 ret. jnys. daily

LEADENHALL STREET & BLACKWALL

3½	R. Lambert	5301, 5302, 5303 (6-6)	12 ret. jnys. daily
3¼	J. Thorogood	5315 (12-3)	5 ret. jnys. daily
3¼	J. Thorogood	5328 (10-2)	5 ret. jnys. daily

PICCADILLY (Gloucester Coffee House) & BLACKWALL

6	G. Barnett	5304, 5365 (12-3)	10 ret. jnys. daily
6	T. Allard	5311 (12-3)	3 ret. jnys. daily
6	J. Hendricks	5316, 5321 (12-3)	6 ret. jnys. daily
6	S. Underwood	5317, 5334, 5356 (12-3)	12 ret. jnys. daily
6	W. Cobb	5320 (12-3)	4 ret. jnys. daily
6	J. Nelson	5323, 5358 (12-3)	6 ret. jnys. daily
6	G. Ellis	5330 (12-3)	3 ret. jnys. daily
6	S. Douglass	5331, 5363 (12—)	8 ret. jnys. daily
6	A. Scott	5340 (12-3)	3 ret. jnys. daily
6	J. Morland	5345 (12-3)	3 ret. jnys. daily
6	T. Fardell	5353, 5354, 5370, 5371, 5372, 5373 (12-3)	24 ret. jnys. daily
6	R. Spyers	5367 (12-3)	4 ret. jnys. daily
6	J. Thorogood	5322, 5324, 5351, 5359, 5319, 5346 (12-3)	30 ret. jnys. daily

OXFORD STREET (Bond Street) & BLACKWALL

6¼	W. Hitchcock	5337 (12-3)	3 ret. jnys. daily

OXFORD STREET (Duke Street) & BLACKWALL

7	W. Stuchfield	5333 (11-1)	3 ret. jnys. daily
7	T. Wilson	5338, 5366 (12-3)	6 ret. jnys. daily

LEADENHALL STREET & BOW

3½	T. H. Giles	4905, 4982 (6-6)	12 ret. jnys. daily
3½	T. H. Giles	4906, 4948, 4949, 5010 (6-3)	24 ret. jnys. daily

PICCADILLY (Bond Street) & BOW

5¼	A. MacNamara	351 (11-1)	4 ret. jnys. daily

OXFORD STREET (Green Man & Still) & BOW (Plough)

5¼	J. Brown	346 (13-2)	5 ret. jnys. daily
5¾	H. Milner	4983 (13-2)	5 ret. jnys. daily
6	Livesey	4973 (12—)	4 ret. jnys. Mon. to Sat.

ST. PAULS & BRENTFORD

10	J. Attfield	2041 (4-8)	2 ret. jnys. daily
10	W. Cullen	1929 (6-6)	2 ret. jnys. Mon. to Sat., 3 ret. jnys. Sun.

BANK & BRENTFORD

10½	J. Kidd	1930 (12-3)	3 ret. jnys. Mon. to Sat., 4 ret. jnys. Sun.

(continued on next page)

BANK & BRENTFORD — continued

10½	J. Kidd	2201 (12-3)	3 ret. jnys. Mon. to Sat., 4 ret. jnys. Sun.
10½	H. Mayo	1953, 1955 (12-3)	8 ret. jnys. daily

GRACECHURCH STREET & BRIXTON

4½	G. Hewett	1305 (6-9)	6 ret. jnys. Mon. to Sat., 1 ret. jny. Sun.
4½	G. Hewett	1441 (6-9)	2 ret. jnys. daily
5	W. Martin	1286 (12-3)	5 ret. jnys. daily
5	W. Martin	1285, 1287, 1304 (6-9)	15 ret. jnys. daily
5	M. Balls	1306, 1307, 1465 (6-9)	15 ret. jnys. daily
5	M. Balls	1308, 1365, 1414 (12-3)	15 ret. jnys. daily
5	T. F. Balls	1313 (12-3)	5 ret. jnys. daily
5	H. Kendall	1402 (12-3)	5 ret. jnys. daily

FLEET STREET & BRIXTON

4½	G. Hewitt	1290 (6-9)	1 ret. jny. Mon. to Sat, 2 ret. jnys. Sun.

BOW (Church) & BRIXTON

5	G. Hewitt	1300 (6-9)	1 ret. jny. Mon. to Sat.
5½	M. Balls	1470 (6-9)	5 ret. jnys. daily

OXFORD STREET (Green Man & Still) & BRIXTON

5½	W. Martin	1401 (6-9)	5 ret. jnys. daily
5½	W. Walters	1337 (11-1)	4 ret. jnys. Mon. to Sat., 3 ret. jnys. Sun.
5½	W. Walters	1444 (14-1)	4 ret. jnys. Mon. to Sat., 3 ret. jnys. Sun.

HIGH HOLBORN & BRIXTON

5½	W. Walters	1280 (6-6)	3 ret. jnys. Mon. to Sat, 2 ret. jnys. Sun.

GRACECHURCH STREET & BROMLEY

11	J. Gearing	531 (4-8)	2 ret. jnys. daily
11	J. Gearing	463 (6-12)	2 ret. jnys. daily

CHARING CROSS & BROMLEY

12	J. Gearing	444 (6-12)	2 ret. jnys. daily
12	J. Gearing	449 (4-8)	2 ret. jnys. daily
12	W. Pawley	425 (4-8)	1 ret. jny. daily
12	W. Pawley	427 (6-9)	1 ret. jny. daily

BANK & BROMPTON Middx.

4½	W. Kimber	2218 (12-3)	5 ret. jnys. daily

OXFORD STREET (Green Man & Still) & CAMBERWELL

4½	J. Blackwell	1013 (6-6)	4 ret. jnys. daily

GRACECHURCH STREET & CAMBERWELL			
3	W. Jones	1006 (12-3)	6 ret. jnys. daily
3½	J. Blackwell	1057, 1073, 1075 (6-6)	15 ret. jnys. daily
3½	J. Blackwell	1076, 1077 (12 —)	9 ret. jnys. daily
3	W. Shefford	1025, 1026, 1027, 1048, 1060 (6-9)	35 ret. jnys. Mon. to Sat., 15 ret. jnys. Sun.
3	J. Shepherd	1028, 1029 (6-9)	16 ret. jnys. daily
3	J. Shepherd	1030, 1043 (12-3)	16 ret. jnys. daily
3	R. Wright	1042 (12-3)	6 ret. jnys. daily
3	E. Smither	1062 (14-1)	7 ret. jnys. daily
FLEET STREET & CAMBERWELL			
3½	J. Blackwell	1015 (12 —)	5 ret. jnys. daily
CHARING CROSS & CAMBERWELL			
4½	J. Blackwell	1016 (6-6)	5 ret. jnys. daily
KINGSLAND GATE & CAMBERWELL			
5	W. Surrey	1068 (12-3)	4 ret. jnys. daily
BANK & CAMDEN TOWN			
4½	T. Shorter	3209 (12-3)	4 ret. jnys. daily
4¼	W. Harding	3210 (14-1)	5 ret. jnys. daily
4½	W. Harding	3245 (12 —)	4 ret. jnys. daily
KENNINGTON GATE & CAMDEN TOWN			
5½	W. Beamon	22 (11-1)	4 ret. jnys. daily
GRACECHURCH STREET & CARSHALTON			
11	D. Brown	1322, 1324 (4-8)	4 ret. jnys. daily
11	D. Brown	1403 (4-11)	2 ret. jnys. daily
FLEET STREET & CARSHALTON			
12	D. Brown	1321 (4-8)	2 ret. jnys. daily
HOLBORN (Old Bell) & CARSHALTON			
12	W. Shepherd	1416 (4-8)	1 ret. jny. Mon. to Sat., 2 ret. jnys. Sun.
CHARING CROSS & CATSFORD BRIDGE			
8	J. Bryant	544 (6-12)	2 ret. jnys. daily
LEADENHALL STREET & CHELSEA			
5½	G. Childs	1920 (12-3)	4 ret. jnys. daily
5½	G. Childs	1921 (12-3)	4 ret. jnys. daily
5½	J. Gomb	1924 (12-3)	4 ret. jnys. daily
5½	J. Gomb	1989 (12 —)	4 ret. jnys. daily
5½	M. Maslin	1928 (12 —)	2 ret. jnys. daily
5½	J. Cripps	2057 (14-1)	3 ret. jnys. daily
5½	W. Cripps	2157 (14-1)	3 ret. jnys. daily

(continued on next page)

LEADENHALL STREET & CHELSEA - continued

$5\frac{1}{2}$	J. Butcher	2064 (14-1) 5 ret. jnys. daily
$5\frac{1}{2}$	J. Chancellor	1961 (12-) 3 ret. jnys. Mon. to Sat.
$5\frac{1}{2}$	J. Chancellor	1963, 1964 (12-) 6 ret. jnys. Mon. to Sat., 4 ret. jnys. Sun.
$5\frac{3}{4}$	G. Chancellor	1965, 1966, 2198 (12-) 8 ret. jnys. Mon. to Sat., 5 ret. jnys. Sun.

LEADENHALL STREET & CHELSEA (Kings Road)

$4\frac{1}{2}$	T. Taplin	16 (12-) 6 ret. jnys. daily

MILE END GATE & CHELSEA

$6\frac{1}{2}$	J. Chancellor	1943, 1960, 1962, 2151, 2238 (12-) 15 ret. jnys. Mon. to Sat., 6 ret. jnys. Sun.
$6\frac{1}{2}$	G. Chancellor	1967 (14-1) 2 ret. jnys. Mon. to Sat., 3 ret. jnys. Sun.
$6\frac{1}{2}$	G. Chancellor	2087 (12-) 2 ret. jnys. daily
$6\frac{1}{2}$	P. Long	2033, 2034 (12-) 10 ret. jnys. daily
$6\frac{1}{2}$	P. Long	2158 (12-3) 5 ret. jnys. daily
$6\frac{1}{2}$	W. Edwick	2176 (14-1) 3 ret. jnys. Mon. to Sat., 2 ret. jnys. Sun.
$6\frac{1}{2}$	W. Edwick	2256 (13-2) 3 ret. jnys. Mon. to Sat., 2 ret. jnys. Sun.
$6\frac{1}{2}$	G. Childs	1958, 2199 (12-) 6 ret. jnys. Mon. to Sat., 4 ret. jnys. Sun.

ALDGATE (Blue Boar) & CHIGWELL ROW

12	W. Rowlay	4970 (4-11) 1 ret. jny. Mon. to Sat., 2 ret. jnys. Sun.

GRACECHURCH STREET & CLAPHAM

$4\frac{1}{2}$	W. Dale	1355 (6-9) 5 ret. jnys. daily
$4\frac{1}{2}$	B. Reeve	1283 (6-6) 2 ret. jnys. daily
$4\frac{1}{2}$	G. J. Saltwell	1386 (6-6) 4 ret. jnys. daily

BOW (Church) & CLAPHAM

5	G. Heathcote	1262, 1263, 1264 (6-9) 9 ret. jnys. daily

CHARING CROSS & CLAPHAM

$5\frac{1}{2}$	W. Sheldrick	1267 (6-9) 3 ret. jnys. Mon. to Sat.

HOLBORN (Blue Posts) & CLAPHAM

5	W. Dale & Co.	1292 (6-6) 3 ret. jnys. Mon. to Sat., 2 ret. jnys. Sun.
5	J. Blackwell	1471 (6-6) 3 ret. jnys. daily

FLEET STREET & CLAPHAM

$5\frac{1}{2}$	S. Fownes	1311 (6-6) 3 ret. jnys. Mon. to Sat., 2 ret. jnys. Sun.

STRAND (Red Lion) & CLAPHAM

5	S. Fownes	1338 (6-6) 3 ret. jnys. daily

GRACECHURCH STREET & CLAPHAM (Plough)

4	H. Hilliar	1281 (6-6)	5 ret. jnys. daily
4	W. Harris	1377 (14-4)	6 ret. jnys. daily
4	W. Harris	1387, 1389 (12-3)	12 ret. jnys. daily
4	J. Blackwell	1378 (12-3)	4 ret. jnys. daily
4	G. Heathcote	1393, 1394 (12-3)	7 ret. jnys. daily

BOW (Church) & CLAPHAM (Plough)

4½	H. Hilliar	1282 (6-6)	5 ret. jnys. daily

GRACECHURCH STREET & CLAPHAM RISE

3½	R. Boxall	1317, 1339 (6-9)	10 ret. jnys. Mon. to Sat., 6 ret. jnys. Sun.

BISHOPSGATE STREET & CLAPTON

4¼	J. Kerrison	4700, 4701 (6-9)	10 ret. jnys. daily
4½	T. Bryan	4702, 4703, 4727 (6-6)	16 ret. jnys. daily
4¼	J. Breach	4706 (6-6)	4 ret. jnys. Mon. to Sat., 2 ret. jnys. Sun.
4½	J. Newman	4721 (6-6)	6 ret. jnys. daily
4¼	J. Newman	4722 (12-3)	6 ret. jnys. daily
4¾	G. Kendall	4708 (6-6)	4 ret. jnys. daily

OXFORD STREET (Green Man & Still) & CLAPTON

6½	G. Kendall	4707 (6-6)	4 ret. jnys. daily
6½	G. Kendall	4710 (12-3)	4 ret. jnys. daily

STRAND (Red Lion) & CLAPTON

6½	T. Bryan	4705 (6-6)	5 ret. jnys. daily

BISHOPSGATE STREET & CLAPTON GATE

3½	M. Noble	4711 (12-3)	5 ret. jnys. daily
3½	G. Whitbread	4713, 4748 (12-3)	12 ret. jnys. Mon. to Sat., 11 ret. jnys. Sun.
3½	J. Kerrison	4742 (14-1)	5 ret. jnys. daily

GRACECHURCH STREET & CROYDON

10½	W. Inkpen & Co.	1269, 1270 (6-12)	6 ret. jnys. daily
10½	W. Inkpen & Co.	1271, 1273 (4-11)	6 ret. jnys. daily
10½	C. Harber	1274, 1275 (4-11)	6 ret. jnys. daily
10½	C. Harber	1422 (6-12)	3 ret. jnys. daily
10½	G. Matthew	1278 (4-8)	2 ret. jnys. daily

CORNHILL & CROYDON

11	R. Marshall	1445 (10-2)	2 ret. jnys. daily

BANK & CROYDON

11	E. Dodd	1341 (6-6)	3 ret. jnys. daily

OXFORD STREET (Green Man & Still) & CROYDON

11	W. Inkpen & Co.	1082 (4-11)	3 ret. jnys. daily

CHARING CROSS & CROYDON

11	W. Inkpen	1268 (6-12)	3 ret. jnys. daily
11	C. Harber	1446 (6-12)	3 ret. jnys. daily

FLEET STREET & DEPTFORD

$4\frac{1}{2}$	J. Agars	372 (12-3)	5 ret. jnys. daily
$4\frac{1}{4}$	T. Brooker	374 (12-3)	5 ret. jnys. daily
$4\frac{1}{4}$	. Courthope	375 (12-3)	5 ret. jnys. daily
$4\frac{1}{4}$	. Courthope	380 (14-1)	5 ret. jnys. daily
$4\frac{1}{2}$	T. Kemmiss	379 (12-3)	4 ret. jnys. daily
$4\frac{1}{4}$	W. Euins	383 (12-3)	5 ret. jnys. daily

PICCADILLY (Gloster Coffee House) & DEPTFORD

$6\frac{1}{4}$	W. Euins	370 (13-2)	5 ret. jnys. daily
$6\frac{1}{4}$	W. Drake	382 (12—)	3 ret. jnys. daily

PICCADILLY (Gloster Coffee House) & DEPTFORD ROAD

6	T. Euins	371 (13-2)	3 ret. jnys. daily
6	G. Lulham	381 (12-3)	4 ret. jnys. daily

CAMBERWELL & DULWICH

$1\frac{1}{2}$	J. Blackwell	10045 (5-1)	7 ret. jnys. daily

FLEET STREET & DULWICH

6	E. Wheels	1044, 1045 (6-9)	6 ret. jnys. daily

OXFORD STREET (No. 122) & DULWICH

7	E. Wheels	1059 (6-6)	3 ret. jnys. daily

GRACECHURCH STREET & DULWICH EAST

$4\frac{1}{2}$	J. Glover	1012 (6-9)	5 ret. jnys. daily

HOLBORN (Blue Posts) & EALING

9	J. Ives & Co.	2902 (4-8)	2 ret. jnys. daily
9	J. Ives & Co.	2966 (4-11)	2 ret. jnys. daily

ST. PAULS & EALING

10	J. Ives & Co.	1900 (4-8)	1 ret. jny. daily

BANK & EALING

10	J. Ives & Co.	2900 (12-3)	2 ret. jnys. daily
10	J. Ives & Co.	2961 (14-1)	2 ret. jnys. daily

ROYAL EXCHANGE & EAST INDIA DOCKS

$3\frac{1}{2}$	J. Lambert	5300 (6-6)	5 ret. jnys. Mon. to Sat.
$3\frac{1}{2}$	J. Lambert	5314, 5357 (6-3)	10 ret. jnys. Mon. to Sat.

BANK & EDGWARE ROAD

4	T. Bird	10 (14-1)	6 ret. jnys. daily
4	J. Newell	11, 246, 314 (14-1)	15 ret. jnys. daily
4	J. Trevett	12, 13, 14 (14-1)	15 ret. jnys. daily
4	J. Bartlett	151 (14-1)	6 ret. jnys. daily
4	T. Bird	155, 163 (14-1)	12 ret. jnys. daily

(continued on next page)

BANK & EDGWARE ROAD — continued

4	P. Sellick	157, 171, 255 (14-1)	15 ret. jnys. daily
4	J.T. Bolton	156, 160, 235, 312 (14-1)	20 ret. jnys. daily
4	J. Bardell	164, 212 (14-1)	12 ret. jnys. daily
4	R. Carpenter	165 (14-1)	6 ret. jnys. daily
4	J. Hill	167, 266 (14-1)	12 ret. jnys. daily
4	E. Watson	176, 223, 239 (14-1)	15 ret. jnys. daily
4	J. Turnbull	179, 251 (14-1)	12 ret. jnys. daily
4	G. Shillibeer	188, 189 (14-1)	10 ret. jnys. daily
4	J. Bardell	193 (14-1)	5 ret. jnys. daily
4	R. Morgan	195, 221, 256 (14-1)	15 ret. jnys. daily
4	M. Sanderson	199 (14-1)	6 ret. jnys. daily
4	J. Parkes	209, 210, 211 (14-1)	18 ret. jnys. daily
4	S. Taylor	229, 289 (14-1)	12 ret. jnys. daily
4	J. Johnson	233 (14-1)	6 ret. jnys. daily
4	J. Johnson	369 (12—)	6 ret. jnys. daily
4	W. Cowderoy	240, 241 (14-1)	10 ret. jnys. daily
4	W. Cowderoy	291, 292, 293, 294 (14-1)	20 ret. jnys. daily
4	R. Bird	245 (14-1)	6 ret. jnys. daily
4	R. Bird	367 (12 —)	6 ret. jnys. daily
4	S. Gaywood	254 (14-1)	6 ret. jnys. daily

BISHOPSGATE STREET & EDMONTON

8	J. St. John	4331 (12-3)	3 ret. jnys. daily
8	W. Matthews	4393 (6-9)	3 ret. jnys. daily
8	W. Matthews	4397 (12-3)	3 ret. jnys. daily

SNOW HILL & EDMONTON

9	W. Matthews	4316, 4317, 4318, 4320, 4395 (6-9)	15 ret. jnys. daily
9	R. Winder	4309 (6-9)	3 ret. jnys. daily
9	S. & J. Isaac	4312, 4313, 4314 (6-9)	9 ret. jnys. daily
9	J. St. John	4329, 4405 (6-9)	6 ret. jnys. daily
9	J. St. John	4330, 4333 (4-8)	6 ret. jnys. daily
9	J. Willis	4335, 4336 (6-9)	6 ret. jnys. daily

PICCADILLY (Black Bear) & ELEPHANT & CASTLE

2	J. Nelson	18 (4-5)	1 ret. jny. daily

CHARING CROSS & ELTHAM

10	W. S. Jewell	445 (6-9)	1 ret. jny. Mon. to Sat., 2 ret. jnys. Sun.

HOLBORN (The Bell) & ENFIELD

12	J. & W. Glover	4379 (4-11)	2 ret. jnys. daily
12	J. & W. Glover	4380, 4381, 4382 (4-8)	6 ret. jnys. daily

HOLBORN (The Bull) & ENFIELD

13	T. Reynolds	4353 (4-8)	1 ret. jny. Mon. to Sat., 2 ret. jnys. Sun.

SNOW HILL & ENFIELD

13	W. Matthews	4315 (6-9) 2 ret. jnys. daily

BANK & FINCHLEY

10	W. Hutton	3400 (6-9) I ret. jny. Mon. to Sat., 2 ret. jnys. Sun.

BANK & FULHAM

7	S. Mawbey	1905, 1906, 1907, 1909, 2214 (12 —) 20 ret. jnys. daily
7	J. Kempshall	1933 (12 —) 4 ret. jnys. daily
7	J. Kempshall	1911 (12 – 3) 4 ret. jnys. daily
7	W. Blanch	1918 (12 —) 3 ret. jnys. daily
7	W. King	1923 (12 —) 3 ret. jnys. daily
7	W. King	2251 (11 – 1) 3 ret. jnys. daily
7	J. Bartlett	1935, 1936 (12 —) 10 ret. jnys. daily
7	J. Clifton & Co.	2163, 2168 (12 —) 8 ret. jnys. daily
7	J. Patey	2240 (12 —) 3 ret. jnys. daily

GRACECHURCH STREET & GREENWICH

$5\frac{1}{2}$	N. Elms	421 (4-5) 7 ret. jnys. daily
$5\frac{1}{4}$	N. Elms	473 (6-9) 7 ret. jnys. daily
$5\frac{1}{4}$	N. Elms	539 (14-4) 7 ret. jnys. daily
$6\frac{1}{2}$	T. Hattersley	442 (12-3) 5 ret. jnys. daily
$6\frac{1}{2}$	T. Hattersley	459 (6-12) 5 ret. jnys. daily
$6\frac{1}{4}$	T. Hattersley	505 (6-6) 4 ret. jnys. daily
$6\frac{1}{4}$	T. Hattersley	565 (6-9) 5 ret. jnys. daily
$6\frac{1}{4}$	T. Hattersley	571 (14-4) 5 ret. jnys. daily
$6\frac{1}{4}$	J. Wheatley	595, 596, 597, 598, 599 (6-12) 30 ret. jnys. daily
$6\frac{1}{4}$	J. Wheatley	600 (12-3) 6 ret. jnys. daily

CHARING CROSS & GREENWICH

6	J. Wheatley	591 (6-9) 6 ret. jnys. daily

OXFORD STREET (Green Man & Still) & GREENWICH

7	J. Wheatley	587, 588, 589, 590 (12-3) 24 ret. jnys. daily
7	J. Wheatley	593 (12 –) 6 ret. jnys. daily
7	W. Plummer	401 (12-3) 5 ret. jnys. daily
7	J. Matson, Snr.	411 (14-4) 6 ret. jnys. daily
7	G. Shillibeer	616, 617, 618, 619 (12-3) 12 ret. jnys. daily
7	J. Matson, Jnr.	519, 520 (12-3) 12 ret. jnys. daily

SOMERSET HOUSE & GREENWICH

| $6\frac{1}{2}$ | J Matson, Snr. | 409 (10-5) 6 ret. jnys. daily |
| $6\frac{1}{2}$ | J. Matson, Snr. | 410 (6-9) 6 ret. jnys. daily |

PICCADILLY (Regent Circus) & HACKNEY

$5\frac{1}{2}$	J. Winch	4744, 4747 (14-1) 8 ret. jnys. daily

ROYAL EXCHANGE & HACKNEY

3	M. Fulham	4716, 4764 (14-1) 16 ret. jnys. daily
3	M. Fulham	4766 (12-3) 8 ret. jnys. daily
3	J. Barber, Snr.	4712 (12-3) 7 ret. jnys. daily
3	J. Barber, Jnr.	4729, 4732, 4743 (12-3) 21 ret. jnys. daily
3	W. J. Jennings	4774 (6-3) 5 ret. jnys. daily

HOLBORN (Old Bell) & HADLEY

12	J. Horsley & Co.	3200 (6-9) 1 ret. jny. Mon. to Sat.

ALDGATE (Three Nuns) & HADLEY

13	J. Horsley & Co.	3414 (4-5) 1 ret. jny. Mon. to Sat.

TOTTENHAM COURT ROAD (Blue Posts) & HADLEY

13	J. Salmon	3416, 3486 (4-8) 2 ret. jnys. Mon. to Sat., 1 ret. jny. Sun.

MILE END GATE & HAMMERSMITH

8	. Davis & Co.	1952 (12—) 4 ret. jnys. daily
8	J. Williams	2154 (12—) 5 ret. jnys. daily
9	W. Danby	2152, 2153 (12-3) 10 ret. jnys. daily

LEADENHALL STREET & HAMMERSMITH

6	C. Chesterton	1912, 1913, 1914, 2178 (12—) 12 ret. jnys. Mon. to Sat., 9 ret. jnys. Sun.
6	H. Sibley	1937, 1968, 2233 (12—) 15 ret. jnys. daily
6	J. Buckmaster	2237 (14-1) 3 ret. jnys. daily

WHITECHAPEL CHURCH & HAMMERSMITH GATE

6½	R. Francies	2080 (12-3) 5 ret. jnys. daily

CHARING CROSS & HAMPSTEAD

5	A. Hamilton	3204, 3213, 3214, 3215 (6-6) 12 ret. jnys. daily
5	. Nunn & Co.	3216, 3217, 3218, 3222 (6-6) 20 ret. jnys. daily

HOLBORN (Blue Posts) & HAMPSTEAD

5	A. Hamilton	3207, 3225 (6-6) 6 ret. jnys. daily

BANK & HAMPSTEAD

5½	A. Hamilton	3308, 3314 (4-8) 6 ret. jnys. daily
5¼	A. Hamilton	3309, 3320, 3321 (6-6) 9 ret. jnys. daily
5½	A. Hamilton	3311, 3313 (4-11) 6 ret. jnys. daily
5¼	A. Hamilton	3224 (12—) 3 ret. jnys. daily
6	A. Hamilton	3226 (12-3) 3 ret. jnys. daily

WATER LANE & HAMPTON

16	J. Tapps	2063, 2211 (4-8) 3 ret. jnys. daily
16	J. Tapps	2149 (4-11) 1 ret. jny. daily

ST. PAULS & HAMPTON

15¼	W. Sealey	2182 (4-11) 1 ret. jny. daily
16¼	S. Taylor	2037 (4-8) 1 ret. jny. Mon. to Sat.
16¼	S. Taylor	2077 (6-9) 1 ret. jny. daily

ST. PAULS & HAMPTON WICK

| 15 | S. Taylor | 2042 (6-9) 1 ret. jny. Mon. to Sat., 2 ret. jnys. Sun. |

BANK & HARROW

| 13 | C. Hudson | 238 (11-1) 1 ret. jny. daily |

ST. PAULS & HERNE HILL

| 4½ | J. Blackwell | 1080 (6-6) 5 ret. jnys. daily |

BOW (Church) & HERNE HILL

| 5 | J. Blackwell | 1081 (6-9) 1 ret. jny. Mon. to Sat. |

ROYAL EXCHANGE & HIGHBURY BARN

| 3¼ | E. Wilson & Co. | 3403 (6-6) 6 ret. jnys. Mon. to Sat. |

CHARING CROSS & HIGHGATE

| 5 | J. Wiber & Son | 3201 (12-3) 3 ret. jnys. daily |

BANK & HIGHGATE

| 6 | W. Pledger | 3499, 3500 (6-9) 6 ret. jnys. daily |

ROYAL EXCHANGE & HOLLOWAY

4½	E. Wilson & Co.	3402 (12-3) 7 ret. jnys. daily
4	E. Wilson & Co.	3401, 3508 (12-3) 14 ret. jnys. daily
4	E. Wilson & Co.	3404 (6-6) 7 ret. jnys. daily
4	J. Balls	3411, 3509 (12-3) 14 ret. jnys. Mon. to Sat., 2 ret. jnys. Sun.
4	J. Barton	3420 (14-1) 7 ret. jnys. Mon. to Sat., 2 ret. jnys. Sun.
4	W. Whittle	3460 (12-3) 4 ret. jnys. daily

CHARING CROSS & HOLLOWAY

| 4½ | T. Shorter | 3205 (12-3) 4 ret. jnys. daily |
| 5 | E. Wilson & Co. | 3527 (12-3) 6 ret. jnys. daily |

BISHOPSGATE STREET & HOMERTON

| 3½ | J. Mulley | 4767, 4771 (12-3) 14 ret. jnys. daily |

ROYAL EXCHANGE & HOMERTON

| 3½ | H. Hawkins | 4763 (12-3) 6 ret. jnys. daily |

BANK & HORNSEY

6	W. T. East	3417 (6-12) 3 ret. jnys. daily
6	W. T. East	3485 (6-6) 3 ret. jnys. daily
6	W. T. East	3507 (6-9) 2 ret. jnys. daily

HORTON & HOUNSLOW

| 7½ | H. Mayo | 1954 (4-5) 1 ret. jny. Mon. to Sat. |

BISHOPSGATE STREET & HOUNDSFIELD

| 8½ | S. & J. Isaacs | 4310 (12-3) 3 ret. jnys. daily |
| 8¼ | S. & J. Isaacs | 4311 (6-9) 3 ret. jnys. daily |

ISLEWORTH & HOUNSLOW			
2	J. Limpus	10005 (4-2) 5 ret. jnys. daily	

COVENTRY STREET & HOUNSLOW		
10	H. Limpus	2242 (6-9) 3 ret. jnys. daily

ST. PAULS & HOUNSLOW		
12	H. Limpus	2243 (6-6) 3 ret. jnys. daily

ST. PAULS & HOUNSLOW BARRACKS		
13	H. Limpus	1947 (6-9) 1 ret. jny. daily
13	H. May	1956, 2245 (6-9) 4 ret. jnys. daily

BANK & HOUNSLOW BARRACKS		
13½	E. Stuchbery & Co.	1971 (12-3) 1 ret. jny. Mon. to Sat., 2 ret. jnys. Sun.

ALDGATE (The Bull) & ILFORD		
7½	A. Hone	5014 (4-8) 2 ret. jnys. daily

COVENTRY STREET & ISLEWORTH		
9	J. Limpus	1980 (6-6) 2 ret. jnys. daily

ST. PAULS & ISLEWORTH		
11	J. Limpus	2002 (6-6) 2 ret. jnys. Mon. to Sat., 3 ret. jnys. Sun.
11	J. Limpus	1976, 2003, 2209 (6-9) 4 ret. jnys. Mon. to Sat., 5 ret. jnys. Sun.

BANK & ISLEWORTH		
12	J. Limpus	1974, 1978 (12-3) 4 ret. jnys. daily

ELEPHANT AND CASTLE & ISLINGTON		
3	C. Morrison	21, 274 (12—) 14 ret. jnys. daily
3	W. Hughes	182, 316, 322 (11-1) 18 ret. jnys. daily
3	J. Wells & Co.	260, 271 (12—) 12 ret. jnys. daily
3	W. E. Coleman	268 (12—) 7 ret. jnys. daily
3	T. Cowling	279 (12—) 6 ret. jnys. daily
3	J. Wells, Snr.	285, 299, 339 (12—) 18 ret. jnys. daily
3	G. Shillibeer	28, 330, 331 (12—) 14 ret. jnys. daily
3	A. B. Gray	362 (12-3) 7 ret. jnys. daily
3	C. F. Hyrons	363 (14-1) 7 ret. jnys. daily

HOLBORN BRIDGE & KENNINGTON		
2½	A. B. Gray	27 (12-3) 6 ret. jnys. daily

KINGS CROSS & KENNINGTON		
17	R. Hedges	17 (12—) 6 ret. jnys. daily

BANK & KENSINGTON		
7	J. Buckmaster	2907 (12-3) 3 ret. jnys. daily
7	J. Buckmaster	2910 (14-1) 3 ret. jnys. daily
7	R. Alderson	2944 (12-3) 3 ret. jnys. daily

BANK & KENTISH TOWN		
5½	J. Wiber & Son	3202,3230,3244 (14-1) 18 ret. jnys. daily

LEADENHALL STREET & KENTISH TOWN		
5½	Jas. Bardell	3211,3227 (12-3) 8 ret. jnys. daily
5½	Jos. Bardell	3219,3228,3233,3239 (14-1) 20 ret. jnys. daily
5½	T. Purdey	3240 (14-1) 5 ret. jnys. daily
5½	S. Gaywood	3241 (12—) 6 ret. jnys. daily
5½	J. Arnold	3243 (12-3) 4 ret. jnys. Mon. to Sat., 2 ret. jnys. Sun.

GRACECHURCH STREET & KENT ROAD		
3	T. Densham	440, 453 (14-4) 12 ret. jnys. daily

STRAND (Red Lion) & KENT ROAD		
4½	T. Densham	455 (12-3) 6 ret. jnys. daily

BANK & KEW BRIDGE		
9	A. Mitchell	1917 (12-3) 3 ret. jnys. daily
9	T. Powell	1938,1940,2169 (12—) 12 ret. jnys. daily
9	W. Collier	1951,1969,1970,2166 (12—) 20 ret. jnys. daily
9	G. Cloud	2073 (12—) 5 ret. jnys. daily
9	T. Fitkin	2119 (12-3) 5 ret. jnys. daily
9	W. Dancer	2183 (12—) 5 ret. jnys. daily

BANK & KILBURN		
6	T.S. Wall	3122 (14-1) 3 ret. jnys. daily
6	R. Trevett	3124 (14-1) 5 ret. jnys. daily

BISHOPSGATE STREET & KINGSLAND		
2½	W. Spinks	4350,4377 (12-3) 10 ret. jnys. Mon. to Sat., 1 ret. jny. Sun.

GRACECHURCH STREET & KINGSTON		
12	W. Benner & Co.	1815 (6-12) 1 ret. jny. Mon. to Sat., 2 ret. jnys Sun.

ROYAL EXCHANGE & LEYTON		
7	R. Wragg	4726 (6-6) 3 ret. jnys. daily

CHEAPSIDE & LEE		
6¾	C. Collins	438 (6-9) 7 ret. jnys. Mon. to Sat.

CHARING CROSS & LEE		
7¾	W. Plummer	402 (6-9) 10 ret. jnys. daily

GRACECHURCH STREET & LEWISHAM		
6½	J. Driver	436 (6-12) 5 ret. jnys. daily

CHARING CROSS & LEWISHAM		
7½	F. Bryant	406 (6-9) 4 ret. jnys. daily
8¼	S. Stilwell	447 (6-9) 3 ret. jnys. daily

ELEPHANT AND CASTLE & LISSON GROVE

4½	J. Trevett	15 (14-1) 5 ret. jnys. daily
4½	. Leonard	247, 257 (12 —) 10 ret. jnys. daily
4½	J. Hill	159 (14-1) 6 ret. jnys. daily
4½	J. Hill	267, 275 (12 —) 12 ret. jnys. daily
4½	J. Hill	281 (14-1) 6 ret. jnys. daily
4½	J. Till	180, 297, 298 (12 —) 15 ret. jnys. daily
4½	J. Newell	181 (14-1) 5 ret. jnys. daily
4½	T. Bird	187 (14-1) 6 ret. jnys. daily
4½	J. Waterlow	220, 344, 345 (12 —) 18 ret. jnys. daily
4½	R. Carpenter	232, 311 (12 —) 12 ret. jnys. daily
4½	T. Paragreen	286 (12 —) 6 ret. jnys. daily
4½	H. Fisher	290, 295, 296 (12 —) 18 ret. jnys. daily

BANK & MAIDA HILL

4¼	G. Bingham	252 (14-1) 5 ret. jnys. daily
4¼	G. Bird	310 (14-1) 6 ret. jnys. daily
4½	R. Carpenter	166 (14-1) 6 ret. jnys. daily
4½	J. T. Bolton	183, 353 (14-1) 10 ret. jnys. daily
4½	J. Newell	186 (14-1) 5 ret. jnys. daily
4½	T. Bird	224 (14-1) 6 ret. jnys. daily
4½	J. Johnson	228, 248 (14-1) 12 ret. jnys. daily
4½	J. Bardell	244 (12-3) 5 ret. jnys. daily
4½	R. Blore	287 (14-1) 5 ret. jnys. daily
4½	A. Bray	349 (12-3) 5 ret. jnys. daily
4½	P. Sellick	366 (14-1) 5 ret. jnys. daily
4½	E. Watson	368 (14-1) 5 ret. jnys. daily

GRACECHURCH STREET & MERTON

8½	T. & S. Holden	1251 (4-8) 2 ret. jnys. daily

OXFORD STREET (Bond Street) & MILE END GATE

4½	R. Rhodes & Co.	19 (14-1) 4 ret. jnys. daily
4½	T. Rowan	20 (14-1) 5 ret. jnys. daily
4½	T. Fisher	25 (14-1) 5 ret. jnys. daily
4½	W. Hattersley & Co.	263 (12-3) 5 ret. jnys. daily

OXFORD STREET (Regent Circus) & MILE END GATE

4¼	Jas. Bardell	194 (12-3) 5 ret. jnys. daily
4¼	Jos. Bardell	196 (13-2) 6 ret. jnys. daily
4¼	M. Sanderson	262, 303 (14-1) 10 ret. jnys. daily
4¼	W. Bennett	315, 320, 347 (14-1) 15 ret. jnys. daily

PICCADILLY & MILE END GATE

4	A. MacNamara	24, 351, 364 (12 —) 15 ret. jnys. daily
4	J. Bonner	272 (14-1) 4 ret. jnys. daily

HOLBORN (Blue Posts) & MILL HILL			
10	W. Woolley	3212 (6-12)	1 ret. jny. daily
GRACECHURCH STREET & MITCHAM			
9	T. & S. Holden	1250 (6-12)	2 ret. jnys. daily
9	T. & S. Holden	1253, 1254 (4-8)	4 ret. jnys. daily
9	T. & S. Holden	1255, 1410 (4-5)	4 ret. jnys. daily
SOMERSET HOUSE & MITCHAM			
9¼	T. & S. Holden	1256 (4-11)	2 ret. jnys. daily
9¼	T. & S. Holden	1415 (4-5)	2 ret. jnys. daily
BANK & MUSWELL HILL			
6½	W.T. East	3418 (6-9)	3 ret. jnys. daily
6½	W.T. East	3419 (6-12)	3 ret. jnys. daily
BANK & NEW HAMPTON			
15½	T. Bull	1931 (12-3)	2 ret. jnys. daily
BANK & NEWINGTON GREEN			
3	E. Lapwood	3412 (12-3)	6 ret. jnys. daily
3	E. Lapwood	4345 (4-11)	7 ret. jnys. Mon. to Sat., 6 ret. jnys. Sun.
OXFORD STREET (Green Man & Still) & NORWOOD			
9	W. Moseley & Co.	1024 (10-5)	2 ret. jnys. daily
9	W. Moseley & Co.	1391 (4-11)	3 ret. jnys. daily
9½	W. Moseley & Co.	1423 (4-8)	2 ret. jnys. daily
FLEET STREET & NORWOOD			
8½	J. Mosely	1289 (4-11)	2 ret. jnys. daily
8½	G. Glover	1031 (4-8)	2 ret. jnys. daily
9	G. Glover	1032 (4-11)	2 ret. jnys. daily
GRACECHURCH STREET & NORWOOD			
6½	G. Glover	1033, 1472 (4-8)	4 ret. jnys. daily
8	G. Glover	1034 (4-8)	2 ret. jnys. daily
9	G. Glover	1035 (4-8)	2 ret. jnys. daily
MILE END GATE & NOTTING HILL			
7	C. Horwood & Co.	2932, 2945 (14-1)	10 ret. jnys. daily
7	C. Horwood & Co.	2946 (14-1)	4 ret. jnys. daily
BANK & PADDINGTON			
4½	T. Purday	3850 (14-1)	6 ret. jnys. daily
4½	P. Sellick	3852, 3900 (14-1)	10 ret. jnys. daily
4½	J. Bull	3853, 3856, 3858, 3897 (14-1)	24 ret. jnys. daily
4½	E. Salmon	3854, 3931, 3935 (14-1)	18 ret. jnys. daily
4½	H. Knapp	3855 (14-1)	5 ret. jnys. daily

(continued on next page)

BANK & PADDINGTON — continued

4½	G. Smith	3859, 3860, 3861 (12–3) 15 ret. jnys. daily
4¼	J. Hands	3862, 3888, 3890, 3891 (14–1) 19 ret. jnys. daily
4½	F. Procktor	3864 (14–1) 5 ret. jnys. daily
4¼	J. Fisher	3877 (14–1) 5 ret. jnys. daily
4¼	T. S. Wall	3886, 3889 (14–1) 10 ret. jnys. daily
4¼	R. Carpenter	3885, 3906, 3915, 3938 (14–1) 24 ret. jnys. daily
4¼	J. T. Bolton	3892, 3893, 3941, 3942 (14–1) 20 ret. jnys. daily
4¼	J. Waterlow	3895, 3896 (14–1) 12 ret. jnys. daily
4¼	G. Mills	3898, 3899 (14–1) 12 ret. jnys. daily
4¼	H. Cook	3903 (14–1) 5 ret. jnys. daily
4½	H. Edmonds & Co.	3904, 3905 (14–1) 10 ret. jnys. daily
4½	J. Trevett	3907, 3908, 3909 (14–1) 15 ret. jnys. daily
4½	D. Hone	3912 (14–1) 5 ret. jnys. daily
4¼	S. Knapp & Co.	3927 (14–1) 5 ret. jnys. daily
4¼	. Boissonade	3939 (14–1) 5 ret. jnys. daily
4¼	J. Turnbull	3865 (14–1) 5 ret. jnys. daily
4½	S. Taylor	3868, 3869 (14–1) 12 ret. jnys. daily
4½	S. Pierce	3871, 3878, 3879, 3880, 3881, 3882 (14–1) 30 ret. jnys. daily
4½	S. Pierce	3933 (12–) 5 ret. jnys. daily
4¼	S. Gaywood	3874 (14–1) 6 ret. jnys. daily

GRACECHURCH STREET & PECKHAM RYE

4¼	J. Prince	1009, 1037, 1039, 1041, 1084 (6–9) 20 ret. jnys. daily
4¼	J. Prince	1038, 1040 (14–1) 8 ret. jnys. daily
4¼	T. E. Tanner	1050 (6–9) 5 ret. jnys. daily
4¼	H. Drew	1053 (6–9) 5 ret. jnys. daily
4¼	H. Drew	1083 (12–3) 5 ret. jnys. daily
4¼	E. Tanner	1054, 1055 (6–9) 10 ret. jnys. daily
4¼	C. Tanner	1065 (6–9) 6 ret. jnys. daily

FLEET STREET & PECKHAM RYE

4¼	T. Ellwood	1072 (6–9) 5 ret. jnys. daily

GRACECHURCH STREET & PECKHAM GROVE

3	D. G. Jackson	1000 (14–4) 3 ret. jnys. Mon. to Sat.
3	D. G. Jackson	1067 (13–2) 6 ret. jnys. daily
3	G. Ross & Co.	1049 (14–4) 7 ret. jnys. daily
3	J. P. Young	1056 (14–4) 8 ret. jnys. daily

OXFORD STREET (Green Man & Still) & PECKHAM GROVE

4¼	D. G. Jackson	1063 (11–1)	3 ret. jnys. Mon. to Sat., 4 ret. jnys. Sun.

ALDGATE (The Bull) & PICCADILLY

3	J. Nelson	206 (4-2)	1 ret. jny. Mon. to Sat.
3	J. Nelson	328 (4-8)	2 ret. jnys. daily

INDIA HOUSE & PIMLICO

4½	W. H. Miller	29 (12-3)	5 ret. jnys. daily

WHITECHAPEL (Church) & PIMLICO (Ebury Place)

4¼	J. E. Bird	30 (10-2)	4 ret. jnys. daily

LEADENHALL STREET & PLAISTOW

5¼	P. Mayhew	4913 (6-9)	4 ret. jnys. daily

BANK & PUTNEY

7	C. Wernsley	2022 (12 –)	1 ret. jny. Mon. to Sat., 2 ret. jny. Sun.
7	J. Goodwin	2078 (4-8)	6 ret. jnys. daily

BANK & REGENT CIRCUS (Oxford Street)

2¼	S. Wimbush & Co.	249 (12 –)	6 ret. jnys. Mon. to Sat.

ST. PAULS & RICHMOND

11	G. Tolley	1915 (6-6)	1 ret. Mon. to Sat., 2 ret. jnys. Sun.
11	J. Littlewood & Co.	1986 (6-6)	4 ret. jnys. daily
11	S. Taylor	2036 (12 –)	3 ret. jnys. daily
11	S. Taylor	2038, 2174 (4-8)	6 ret. jnys. daily
11	S. Taylor	2049, 2219 (6-6)	6 ret. jnys. daily
11	W. Sealy	2265 (4-8)	3 ret. jnys. daily
12	R. Ayling	1934 (6-9)	2 ret. jnys. daily

BANK & RICHMOND

11¼	J. Costelow	2194 (12-3)	2 ret. jnys. daily
11½	S. Taylor	2252 (14-1)	3 ret. jnys. daily

ST. PAULS & ROEHAMPTON

8	E. Dawney	1973 (6-6)	1 ret. jny. Mon. to Sat., 2 ret. jny. Sun.

ALDGATE (Saracens Head) & ROMFORD

12	E. Deacon & Co.	4951 (4-11)	2 ret. jnys. daily

BANK & ST. JOHNS WOOD

5	J. Williams	3873 (5-10)	3 ret. jnys. daily
5	R. Carpenter	3884 (6-9)	6 ret. jnys. daily
5	H. Edmonds & Co.	3901 (14-1)	5 ret. jnys. daily

ELEPHANT AND CASTLE & ST. JOHNS WOOD

5	J. Leonard	158 (12 –)	5 ret. jnys. daily

BISHOPSGATE STREET & SHACKLEWELL		
3	W. Spinks	4328 (12-3) 5 ret. jnys. Mon. to Sat.
ROYAL EXCHANGE & SNARESBROOK		
7¼	T. Brotherhood & Co.	4917, 4918 (4-8) 4 ret. jnys. daily
SYBORNE'S CORNER & SNARESBROOK		
2	R. Wragg	10006 (4-5) 4 ret. jnys. Mon. to Sat., 3 ret. jnys. Sun.
BANK & SOUTHALL		
13	J. Roach	2933 (12-3) 2 ret. jnys. Mon. to Sat., 1 ret. jny. Sun.
SNOW HILL & SOUTHGATE		
11	W. Pickard	4403 (6-9) 1 ret. jny. Mon. to Sat.
12	W. Matthews	4322, 4323 (6-9) 5 ret. jnys. daily
BANK & STAMFORD HILL		
4	W. F. Finch	4398 (12-3) 6 ret. jnys. daily
OXFORD STREET (Boar & Castle) & STANMORE		
11	M. Sanderson & Co.	3101 (4-8) 1 ret. jny. daily
BANK & STOKE NEWINGTON		
3½	L. Willan	4305, 4306 (12-3) 11 ret. jnys. Mon. to Sat., 5 ret. jnys. Sun.
3⅝	W. Spinks	4327 (12-3) 6 ret. jnys. daily
3¼	J. Kirby	4345 (12-3) 6 ret. jnys. daily
3⅞	F. Baker & Co.	4370 (12-3) 5 ret. jnys. Mon. to Sat., 1 ret. jny. Sun.
3½	W. F. Finch	4399 (6-9) 6 ret. jnys. daily
PICCADILLY (Regent Circus) & STOKE NEWINGTON		
5¼	L. Willan	4307 (12-3) 1 ret. jny. Mon. to Sat.
GRACECHURCH STREET & STREATHAM		
7	W. Inkpen & Co.	1376 (4-8) 3 ret. jnys. daily
7	W. Duwden	1368 (6-9) 3 ret. jnys. Mon. to Sat., 2 ret. jnys. Sun.
7	W. Duwden	1369 (6-9) 1 sgl. jny. Mon. to Sat., 2 ret. jnys. Sun.
BOW (Church) & STREATHAM		
7¼	W. Duwden	1370 (6-9) 1 sgl. jny. Mon. to Sat.
FLEET STREET & SYDENHAM		
9	H. Doo	1017 (6-12) 1 ret. jny. daily
9	H. Doo	1018 (4-8) 2 ret. jnys. daily
OXFORD STREET (Green Man & Still) & SYDENHAM		
9½	H. Doo	1058 (4-8) 1 ret. jny. daily
PICCADILLY (Regent Circus) & TOTTENHAM		
8	L. Willan	3524 (6-6) 3 ret. jnys. daily

158

BISHOPSGATE STREET & TOTTENHAM GREEN		
5	G. Sumpter	4301(12-3) 5 ret. jnys. Mon. to Sat., 4 ret. jnys. Sun.
5	G. Sumpter	4344(6-9) 5 ret. jnys. Mon. to Sat., 4 ret. jnys. Sun.
FLEET STREET & TOOTING		
7¼	T.&S. Holden	1252 (4-8) 2 ret. jnys. daily
HOLBORN (Blue Posts) & TOTTERIDGE		
11½	R. Davis	3516 (12-3) 1 ret. jny. Mon. to Sat., 2 ret. jnys. Sun.
BANK & TURNHAM GREEN		
8	G. Cloud	1927, 2066, 2071, 2177 (12-3) 20 ret. jnys. daily
8	G. Cloud	2067, 2068, 2069, 2070, 2072, 2074, 2075, 2076, 2162 (12—) 45 ret. jnys. daily
8	T. Fitkin	2213 (12-3) 5 ret. jnys. daily
8	J. Hardwick	2260 (12—) 5 ret. jnys. daily
ST. PAULS & TWICKENHAM		
12½	J. Littlewood	1988 (6-9) 4 ret. jnys. daily
12¼	W. Sealey	2191 (4-8) 2 ret. jnys. daily
WATER LANE & TWICKENHAM		
12	J. Tapps	2062 (4-5) 4 ret. jnys. daily
BANK & TWICKENHAM		
13	J. Ware	2164, 2210 (11-1) 4 ret. jnys. daily
ROYAL EXCHANGE & UPTON		
5½	S. Levy	5017 (6-9) 6 ret. jnys. daily
GRACECHURCH STREET & VASSAL ROAD		
3	G. Hewitt	1442 (14-1) 6 ret. jnys. Mon. to Sat., 4 ret. jnys. Sun.
OXFORD STREET (Green Man & Still) & VAUXHALL		
3¼	W.H. Ball	197, 317 (13-2) 12 ret. jnys. daily
4	J. Wheatley	191 (13-2) 6 ret. jnys. Mon. to Sat., 2 ret. jnys. Sun.
4	W.H. Ball	243 (13-2) 6 ret. jnys. daily
STRAND (Red Lion) & VAUXHALL		
3	J. Wheatley	170 (13-2) 5 ret. jnys. Mon. to Sat., 2 ret. jnys. Sun.
GRACECHURCH STREET & VAUXHALL		
2¼	J. Wheatley	192 (13-2) 6 ret. jnys. Mon. to Sat., 2 ret. jnys. Sun.
BANK & VAUXHALL		
3	J. Haslett	237 (13-2) 7 ret. jnys. Mon. to Sat.